WELCOME TO
DONJONG HEIGHTS

ENJOY YOUR STAY

BEN BOREK

Donjong Heights

egg
box
PUBLISHING

Donjong Heights

First Published, 2007, by Egg Box Publishing
www.eggboxpublishing.com
Reprinted 2007

Book Design:
Nathan Hamilton

Artwork:
© Natalie Fernandes & Matt Croft
at Illustration Zoo

Printed and bound by:
Biddles, Kings Lynn
www.biddles.co.uk

ISBN: 978-0954392-02-4

Acknowledgements

Thanks to George Szirtes, to Denise Riley, to Annika for her tolerance, to Nathan for liking it, to Alex Coxen, and to Edmund for much, not least for severing his finger in my company.

To my friends.

"When all is said and done, more is said than done."
Lou Holtz

Donjong Heights

a novel in verse

by Ben Borek

Prologue

Wherein we are introduced to Donjong Heights

South London has its reputation:
 No tube, a multitude of guns,
 And hence this Johnsonesque quotation:
"When Peckham tires one simply runs
On up to Hoxton and carouses
In trendy noveau-cool warehouses
And listens to Electro Funk
Affecting toned down retro-punk."
Don't get me wrong, it's no Soweto
Down south, it's not all crack and pillage –
Just take a look at Dulwich Village –
But for the common man it's Netto,
Not Conran, tea, not mochaccino,
And Asda jeans, not Valentino.

Now Reader, focus on a room;
Mix cinematic metaphors
With bookish ones, engage your zoom
And speed up pockmarked streets, through doors
That open for the lens politely,
Skim rooftops high above the nightly
Dramatics in the streets below
(The pubs call time, the usual show
Of fights and mawkish "au revoirs!"),
Then hurtle up, the revellers melt
And fade behind, Orion's belt
Is slalomed briskly and the stars
Are left to their portentous glowing
As, Reader, look, the camera's slowing...

It crawls towards a grotty dwelling,
An edifice of brick and rot,
Pads through a smashed-in doorway smelling –
Predictably, I know, but not
Untrue – whichever one that you're in,
All council estates reek of... urine.
The lift is out of order, so
The camera has to boldly go
Up nine levels and past nine landings
On stairs now lacking banisters,
Now strewn with needles, canisters
That once held paint (now used for brandings
Of off-white walls with 'YPB',
'Regret', 'KondemOne RIP'),

And spins round ninety slow degrees,
Meanders on through several halls
Where dust-soaked amber filigrees
From strip-lights bolted to the walls
Provide our scene's dim source of lighting.
One doorway bares a plaque inviting:
Come on Punk, rob me, make my day.
And now the soundtrack starts to play
With added, looming, grave intensity –
As you'll have noted, there's not been
A tune picked for this opening scene...
Choose one yourself with the propensity
To build a sense of introspection
And melancholy from your collection...

Perhaps a moody saxophone
From John Coltrane, perhaps some strings,
A cello's poignant rising drone,
Some ambient electronic pings,
A Deep House track that hypnotises
Or Radiohead's 'No Surprises',
Or anything by Portishead,
Or Leonard Cohen... As I've said,
The choice is yours... but just make sure
That now you fade it out quite gently...
As here the camera stops intently
Before our goal, a mottled door;
It hovers, ponders what to do...
With one last surge it ghosts right through.

Inside, beneath a pale fluorescent
Lamp-glow: our tale's protagonist.
His smoking – furious, incessant –
Has filled the scene with fine-knit mist.
The camera, now with gentle panning,
Investigates the chamber: spanning
One wall, above the fireplace,
A giant print: Schiele's *Embrace*;
Three photographs (a girl with braided
Blond hair, a coastal shot of Nice,
A sunset) share the mantelpiece;
Some books... but here the shot grows faded...
And after all, it's getting late...
Our subject speaks. Let him narrate.

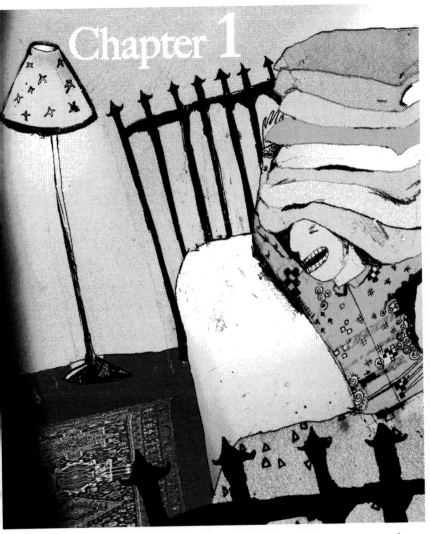

Chapter 1

Wherein we meet our hero

So what, my faulty, lame aorta,
My crushed left ventricle? My heart
Continues ticking as it ought to,
Does not impinge upon the art
Of human form in mortal, glorious
Lithe grace. Though prone to wax censorious
("Twin Devils grog and Old Holborn!")
Dear Doc, it's none of your concern.
And, noted as your warnings are,
I'll leave my fate in casual sway
To thrust itself into my way
(I could be hit by bus or car).
So; 'Excess, Wisdom', pace Blake,
I'll sup delight for its own sake.

So here you have my manifesto,
A sketch of my philosophy,
And Reader, now it's time, you'd best know
My situation, mode de vie.
My dwellings: brick, London SE,
Where bourgeois neighbours *cockerney*
And darlings mingle with old mates
In opulence and rough estates.
My tower block alone: Japan,
Mauritius, Chad, the Sikhs, the Moors,
All post their envoys to its floors.
The requisite lone Rastaman
Completes this Commonwealth, of sorts,
Of *haute couture* and raucous sports.

II

Invading my tenth-storey room
Each evening (no account for taste),
The rumblings of frenetic doom:
The horror that is "Drum 'n' Bass".
The culprit is uncouth Tyrone,
Who, though sixteen, lives quite alone
(Mum disappeared "long time ago"
His father he is yet to know),
Though through the stolid concrete frumpery,
March trails of mini-skirted harlots;
Chantelles, Candices, Chloes, Charlottes
Provide Tyrone with boisterous company.
From dusk 'til dawn they booty-shake
And keep their host's eyes wide-awake.

I rarely gather what transpires
Behind the double-bolted door
Unless Tyrone's huge amp conspires
To blow, then audible, the roar
Of host and unnamed guest, gymnastically
Engaged most unecclesiastically.
Shrill yelps and groans express a measure
Of, I surmise, a mutual pleasure.
Young lion servicing his pride!
And with these youngsters with the horn
Not climaxing till after dawn,
Defending sleep and dreams, I hide,
Ear-plugged and buried in my bed,
Eight pillows stacked upon my head.

Before describing all the rest,
The things that happen in my block,
I must get something off my chest:
You note, above, I mentioned Doc.
He specialises in all things
Of cardiac import at King's
(King's College Hospice, Camberwell).
It's safe to say my heart's not well.
The Doc (his full name: William Wyatt),
When faced with disbelief's bravado
("I'll drink red wine, eat avocado!"),
Keeps all his fears and warnings quiet.
He sees no use in admonition
For me with my unique condition.

He reads my notes with fascination.
He's well and truly mystified.
My heart won't heed his ministrations,
Reacts to nothing he has tried.
He'll stroke his chin with chubby fingers,
Trawl through his beard, its russets, gingers,
Paprika reds, and odd white strands,
Then place his head within his hands
To hide his now bewildered face
Betraying deep internal grumbling,
He says, "Aaah... It appears I'm stumbling
To recollect another case
Whose symptoms parallel your own.
Give me a week or two, I'll phone

Around and ask some learned peers,
See if they haven't any thoughts
On ways to dissipate your fears,
My puzzlement should come to naught.
I'll ask my wife (a doctor too),
My son (he's based at Waterloo
Infirmary), can't hurt to chance it,
I'll check back-issues of *The Lancet.*
Between them all we'll shed some light
On this conundrum in your chest.
Leave it with me, I'll do my best
To help alleviate your plight."
This conversation was in June,
And I had hoped to hear back soon

As poss. from my bewildered Doc.
But, three months later, it's September,
The diagnosis is: still crock.
I'm losing faith and can't remember
The sense of nonchalance I had
("I'll see the Doc, it won't be bad").
I'm overtired and rarely cheerful
And often find myself quite tearful.
I've lost all vigour, lost all vim,
My energy has gone, this state
Of ignorance has come to grate.
I'm now inclined to gravely swim
In my ennui's deep, dark recesses
As my aorta retrogresses.

And now a me-less future looms
About my daily thoughts. This sentiment
Now seems concrete, inhabits rooms,
Pervades the elevated tenement
In which I daily sit and dwell:
"Why is it me who's so unwell?"
I know this focusing on troubles
Results in a tristesse that doubles
It's size with every mental leap,
Yet, for a man in my position,
No consolation of religion,
My only solace is in sleep.
Oh sleep! In sleep, perchance to dream
I've been removed from this whole scene.

I met the Doc again last week
In his salubrious top-floor nest
Decked out with leather couches, teak
Sideboards, an ancient Georgian desk.
Old Periodicals, the mainly
Medical, were strewn insanely
Across his tea-stained Turkish rug.
There, something spoke from Wyatt's shrug,
The way his beard appeared so wild,
Its whiskers with their own tenacity
To swirl round madly. Strained mordacity
Had overcome him. Though he smiled
Benignly, it was plain to see
All was not well. "Doc, talk to me!

"Now what's up? I anticipate
From your demeanour, Dearest Bill,
Your scatty and dishevelled state,
The news you have for me is ill."
"The news is ill and so are you,
There's really nothing I can do.
I'm sorry, son, but you're a mystery,
I've never seen in all my history..."
(And at this point the Doc's voice wavered
Like *he* was ill, eyes full of tears)
"... In all my time, throughout my years..."
His face was pained, his words were laboured,
"... Of work, I never chanced to know
A heart so dead intent to slow."

"To slow? You What! Doc... are you crazy?
Now, hearts don't simply slow right down,
They don't just suddenly get lazy!"
The Doc affected such a frown,
His forehead was a vast plateau
Where all life now disdained to grow.
The remnants of old thirsty rivers
Cut through the dust in ghastly slivers
Of grim foreboding, resignation.
I sensed an utter loss of hope.
"This wasn't caused by smoking dope –
Some years ago – mere recreation?"
My thoughts began to bend and slip.
I had to talk to keep my grip.

"I can't conceive or chance a guess,
Despite my patent expertise,
At why your heart's no little mess"
(His grave, unwelcome litotes).
"Narcotics don't upset blood pumps
More than, say, pertinacious mumps
In early childhood." More at ease
Now with the technicalities
And science babble, Bill's words flowed
Like water from a bubbling spring.
I was a tiny stone within
That toxic stream. I glimpsed the road
Toward my death: cold, hard and grey
Without a street lamp on the way.

It's time I offered full description
Of my good self, my very nabs,
So that engagement with this fiction
Is more than uninformed blind stabs
Into the dark and ill-lit world
That regularly is unfurled
Inside one's mind when called upon
To draw a mental sketch of one
Unrealistically projected
Within a text. A face is thrown
Up from a list of all those known
By each good reader and selected
To fit the bill: a travesty!
For I am me and only me.

A shell-suit is a fashion crime,
A laughable synthetic fad,
And though I wore one in my time,
Neglecting any sense I had
Of style or modish clothing etiquette,
My blame lies with the loafing social set
To which I was then rather nominally
Attached (we dressed truly abominably).
Now days I'd say I'm more demure.
Without the cliques of teenage years
I try to rise above my peers
And, free from stricture, code and law,
My aim is to impart a style
Both tasteful, smart and casual. While

Some sycophants revere a label
With no consideration for
Its quality, *I* find I'm able
To see beyond a name. The more
Emblazoned with a flashy logo
The more the wearer's bound to forego
A disproportionately high
Expense for what has caught their eye.
Invariably, once home, these goods
Will turn out to be quite ill made
(The seams too loose, the zippers frayed,
Misshapen cuffs and flimsy hoods),
Yes sportswear is the biggest folly:
It's so much crap for so much lolly.

It's good to keep yourself in trim,
Though lately efforts have been curt.
I baulk at visits to the gym,
All those machines, one could get hurt!
I'll still perform a forward roll
When called upon. Cholesterol
Is well in check, BP is low
(And getting rapidly more so).
There's nothing like an early jog
To banish morning's bleary listlessness
That swims about my troubled consciousness
Like deep and dense lethargic fog
(Though now I manage little more
Than downstairs, then back to my floor).

All very well this exercise
Of languid limbs and phlegm-logged lungs
But, really, when the eager eyes
Transport across the spectral rungs
Of learning's stepladder towards
The boughs and branches, vines and chords
Of thought's forever-sprouting Redwood –
That's working out! I find the deadwood
Of tactile flesh and muscle tiring.
Why toil with treadmills or Pilates
When one could learn that 'kubernates'
Is ancient Greek for helmsman? Firing
The cultured clay of books and letting
The kiln of thought boil – now that's sweating...

"Which books?" you ask, "which glittering names
Can stir, console, revive, and awe me?"
I steer away from Henry James
(His noble rambling tends to bore me –
Perhaps the failing's mine, not his?
That's fine, each to his own, what is
Opinion if it must be learnt
From outside sources and not burned
Upon each man's subjective retina?)
My penchants? Baudelaire, Flaubert,
Camus, Collette, Apollinaire.
So, Reader, now, you must be Getting a
Sense of my love for Gallic art!
My one bugbear is Jean-Paul Sartre.

(His egotism's gross, inane.
Before I pull him from my shelf,
Endure *La Nausée* once again,
I'd think I'd rather shoot myself.
Unlike Camus, he lacks, I find,
All semblance of a balanced mind.
Refuting he was self-obsessed
Compares to saying east and west
Don't lie in polar opposition.
He fuzzies the whole notion "being",
Stops students of *L'Être* from seeing
His philosophical position.
His favourite haughty, glib refrain:
"You know, I have a golden brain!")

In truth, though, I don't find I'm able
To well describe myself at all.
My nickname used to be 'Clark Gable'
(This years ago, in upper school).
The noun that people have found handy
For me, if unenlightened – 'dandy' –
Is superficial, empty, just is
Inadequate to do one justice...
(Oh, how I hate that dumb ascription!)
But anyhow, I'll come a cropper
If I don't now do what is proper.
I'll now defer my own description
To another voice whose range is greater,
The dear *Omniscient Narrator.*

Oh yeth! Tith I, the all theeing eye!
Firtht and foremotht I mutht inform
You, dearetht Reader, of the why
And wherefore of my wordth' thtrange form:
The reathon ith, you won't have mith'ed,
I thuffer with an awful lithp.
No thurgeon'th knife will ever heal it,
And thcarthely can I ever contheal it.
With that done with and by the by,
I'll thtart to lyrically dethcribe
The young man from flat eighty-five:
A lofty home amid the thky,
Hith thkin mottled, hith hair like rutht,
Hith fathe commandth pity and trutht.

We find him in the blacketht thtate,
Tith truly foul and unpropitiouth,
Hith mood, reflected in hith gait
(Leth ponderouth than plain thuthpiciouth),
Thuggethtth a maudlin thenthibility
Imbued with jealouth thenthitivity
(Conthealed from all thuthpecting folkth
Behind the veilth of rueful joketh)
Towardth the world en mathe, but motht
Of all at thothe who take ath read
Their luck, like they'll not thoon be dead
And gone. He knowth he'll thoon be toatht
But thtill needth to apprethiate
It'th not a punithment – it'th fate.

He hathn't honoured, rarely weeping,
Hith parent'th long-thince thcattered dutht.
He'd rather jutht continue thleeping.
But now, ath death drawth clothe, he mutht,
As fate'th mythteriouth purpothe burrowth,
Reap a brief harvetht on their furrowth.
A vocation, true, must thtir hith heart
Before hith time comth to depart,
And leave hith faint footprintth in glory,
Not let hith rage boil in hith room,
One ith a long time in the tomb!
With that let uth rethume our thtory,
Thee if he cannot learn to laugh,
And earn a noble epitaph.

Sometimes I'm not sure what my game is,
Dear Reader, doubts invade my head.
I know that I'm no Martin Amis.
I can't impart impending dread
Or nervous rush into my story,
Can't work in adjectival fury.
In case I haven't made it clear,
Don't underestimate my fear.
I don't know if it must be said
But now I'm stating it explicitly:
I'll soon be wholly, inextricably,
Inanimate, stone cold, quite dead.
So if my emotion has been terse
Blame the restrictions of the verse.

Chapter 2

Wherein our hero has an idea

The convoluted cityscape
  And sky: all panoramic greys.
  The swollen heavens seemed to gape
Wide open. Out poured morning's sprays
Of sun – a blanched and wounded light –
Emerging from an epic fight
With wicked, armoured ranks of tumorous,
Battalions of baleful cumulus,
Their cannons the reporting thunder
Directed by the mighty Thor.
And soon, revived, he's back for more
And pulls the jaded sun back under.
Then battle will ensue again,
Down fall shards of jagged rain.

While outside earth and raincloud fought
Their drizzling war of dank attrition,
I found myself immersed in thought,
As is my vain predisposition
(I stare out, hypnotised, at foggy
Grey dawns, pyjama'd, head still groggy).
And while fixated by a lamp,
My thoughts infused with rising damp
And smells of conflagrated toast:
"I've not long on this mortal coil.
With Christmas looming close, to spoil
The chance of fun, not make the most
Of what may be my last Yuletide
Is something I just won't abide."

To mark the season of our Lord
I think it meet and rather fitting
To gather the erratic horde
Of Donjong Heights and get them sitting
Around a dinner table, mingling,
Exchanging anecdotes and jingling
Their glasses full of schnapps or whisky.
Admittedly this could be risky:
There are some occupants with whom
I've had unpleasant intercourse.
Some others, though, throughout the course
Of passing chats amid the gloom
Of tepid, listless hallway light,
Revealed themselves as civil, polite:

Grey-haired and corpulent, patrician,
Intensely moody, six-feet tall,
With eyes that testify 'perdition',
He lives three doors along the hall.
Once, long ago, an academic,
Until his drunkenness, endemic,
Was round the clock and undisguised,
And one too many ill-advised
And barely sober proposition
Precipitated all his strife.
He lost his nubile post-grad wife,
His fellowship, research position,
His Pembroke house, his Oxford pension,
Developed chronic hypertension.

And here it is, with perfect timing
(Expedient indeed for one
Whose story must be told by rhyming)
His name fits nicely here – it's John.
(It's John J. Johnson on his passport).
His only (unangelic) transport
Is these days gleaned from gin or ales,
Recounting tall, recycled tales
(How in his youth he drank with Gandhi,
Watched Ali box when he was Clay
Was on the knoll when JFK...)
Not heavy with *Onus Probandi*,
But which his placid drinking mate
Feels no compulsion to debate.

They sit, the two of them, conversing
On learned erudite affairs.
John J.'s an expert at dispersing
Drunk barflies with his caustic glares
(Hot laser beams beneath his glasses).
Some afternoons impromptu classes
(*The Sexuality of Words* –
"Did Keats mean Girls when he wrote Birds")
Are held by John. His only pupil
His friend, whose antiquated suits –
Exotic, hand-wrapped thin cheroots –
His lack of any carnal scruple,
Stentorian and ardent Credo –
"Still let me love!" – and vast libido

Have meant he's seen a hefty portion
Of scrapes while in the Gibbon's Head.
His pompous habit – smug retortion
At things a snooker-player's said –
Has, thankfully, been curbed by John
("My dear boy, keep your breeches on!
Don't be so passionately vocal!")
So now, if not a cherished local,
He's tolerated as eccentric –
The oddball type who props up bars
And shows off gaudy battle scars –
Delusional and egocentric.
He's always chasing some young siren
And proudly calls himself Lord Byron.

He, over drinks, scans English verse
With sage, aristocratic airs,
And often draws out from his purse
Snapshots of countless girls he swears
He's loved, all charming, svelte and slender.
With ancient coins, not legal tender,
And dating back two hundred years,
He tries, in vain, to pay for beers.
And with a wistful glint of eye
Remarks to John "That barmaid, Vicky,
She's always eager for a quickie,
John, why don't you give her a try?
I feel you need a youthful lover.
And if not her, why not her brother?"

We're not all born quite who we'd hope we are:
Three doors along my grubby hallway
A girl maintains that Ethiopia
Is home (in fact it's County Galway).
It's rumoured she was christened Kylie,
But K is now H, therefore 'Hylie' –
Her reverential *nom de choix*
(In honour of the Emperor).
Her robes are resolutely green,
And often daubed with lions in red.
On top her fragile, burdened head,
Dreadlocks, their colour: Tangerine.
Her countenance is droll, intense,
As she preaches of Jah, love, incense.

Dear Reader, yeth, again tith I.
Do pleathe forgive this interruption,
But I've been watching from on high,
And feel enthuthed by thith eruption
Of progreth that our thubject'th made.
It theemth hith ill luck hath not weighed
Too heavy on – ahem – hith heart.
And he'th already made a thtart
In theeking to uthe hith time well.
And plauditth are motht greatly due
(Provided he can follow through
Hith plan), ath for him there'th no hell
More gruethome than the preth-ganged jollity
That'th alwayth Chrithtmath party polithy.

Along with these three I'll invite,
In festive spirit, to my home,
For one concessionary night,
Next door's aforementioned Tyrone.
I find him just a little suspect.
His scoffing cocksure pimpled aspect
Does not immediately endear.
There's nothing there that I should fear,
However, and his record collection
Should prove expedient. Gate-crashing
Proceeded by drunk, violent clashing
Concerns me, though – for my protection
I'll call my beefy brother, Chester,
Who earns his crust as a pro-wrestler.

Though me and Chester share a mother,
In truth he's just a demi-sibling,
But he refers to me as "brother"
And I to him – there's rarely quibbling
(Most people seldom start disputes
With one who wears size eighteen boots,
Or criticise or castigate
A man who measures six foot eight).
He's only in the wrestling game
Now that his singing hopes are dashed.
All operatic dreams were crashed
For him one fateful day in Spain
By two sharp horns, their angry owner,
One afternoon in mad Pamplona.

He fights now – though he's one lung short,
This minor problem hasn't hindered
His progress in his chosen sport –
And always leaves the ring uninjured.
Majestically he kicks and gropes
And clambers up the ringside ropes
Then hurtles earthward with a crash,
Performs the "Flying-Elbow Smash".
His taut pectorals, chiselled cheeks,
His torso's burnished, sun-blushed brown,
Draw girls from Cheam to Kentish Town
(On strict rotation of two weeks
He wines and dines and charms them rotten
Then meets their friend and all's forgotten).

His status as a Casanova
Has caused a few fraternal quarrels,
But all my protests soon blow over:
He just has looser sexual morals.
We've had but one momentous spat –
The spark? My erstwhile sweetheart Cat.
She was the cause, one drunken night,
Of mine and Chester's one true fight.
I needn't waste too much line space
(It wouldn't serve to add suspense)
I'll credit readers with the sense
To judge who had the bloodied face,
Who made the trip to A and E,
You'll all have guessed, yes, it was me.

But back to Catherine I veer.
Each eye the deepest azure well.
Each tooth a lustrous pearl. Each ear
A fragile, perfect coral shell.
Each hair a length of golden thread.
Each lip a crimson satin bed.
Each step, so graceful, lithe and delicate,
Could rouse the most short-sighted celibate.
For just a week we were a pair,
Just seven days of dreamy bliss
In which I savoured every kiss
And trembled in her exhaled air.
No sooner had I found my mate,
I lost her on a double date.

We'd met Chester and Isabella
(They too were in a weeklong tryst)
For cocktails in The Smashed Patella
And there things took an awful twist.
It seemed that my capricious brother
Had eyes more for my current lover
Than he did for his own sweetheart.
Poor Izzy! Chester broke her heart.
She left, morose, amid a shower
Of tears, "I really have abhorred
Just sitting here and being ignored,"
Her sobbing parting shot. An hour
Passed by and Chester kept on smarming
At Cat. I found this quite alarming.

And soon I could endure no more.
I felt offended, not just hurting.
Beneath the table (final straw!):
Their feet engaged in ardent flirting.
Through crimson mist, to my surprise,
I hit my bro between the eyes.
An action, I admit, foolhardy,
Precipitated by Bacardi.
A fight ensued, a duel for honour.
I couldn't have him mock, disparage
My love (and wreck a future marriage?)
And I'd have surely been a goner
But Chester's gross inebriation
Impeded his retaliation.

One thing our hero doethn't know –
Chethter wath thtruck with burning shame
And thwore that night to never go
And charm a girl hith brother claimed.
And thith explainth why, to thith day,
Our young man'th not had cauthe to thay
"Chethter, you philanderer, you thwine,
You leave that girl alone, she'th mine!"
But ath for love, it died that night.
Thweet Catherine, thickened by the violenthe,
Ran out the pub in thtartled thilence,
But not before she'd time to write
Upon a beermat to each brother:
"You animalth detherve each other."

I'm sorry, I digress... I'm back
Now in the land of rhyming prose
And on pink parchment with ink (black)
To all concerned I'll now compose
(My caffeine intake has been high
This morning, I've not eaten, I
Fear my calligraphy may slope
And tangle – I just hope they cope)
An invite that is, well, inviting
And open, sympathetic, kind.
Yes, that's the style I have in mind.
It should convey, in simple writing,
The spirit of my Christmas party.
Good fun, of course, but not too tarty:

"Consider something, please, Dear Neighbour,
Before the days of contraception
(A goat bladder *won't* preclude labour),
An unasked-for and chaste conception
Is just not fair! So one abstains in
The name of economics, reins in
All lustful impulses until
Such time as one could proudly fill
An infant's nursery with complete
Accoutrements – a costly, broad
Array of mobiles (reed, wood, gourd) –
Felt booties for the newborn feet,
A pot of savings to assuage
Potential in-roads in one's wage..."

"You do all this, you plan, remaining
Untouched and virginal, you fear
Your Joseph's tired of this refraining
From intercourse (he's been seen near
A seedy bar called Jezebel's
In Nazareth's East End which sells
More than just wine and melon vodka...)
And you yourself have prayed to God to
Impart you with the strength to banish
These thoughts that can't have come from Him –
When Joseph trots in from the gym
You wish his sweaty robes would vanish
And leave him standing virile, braced,
To leave you feeling not so chaste."

"But lo! Before that sore temptation
Has time to even be addressed
A weird nocturnal visitation:
Some chap who's rather oddly dressed
In cambric sheet and strap-on wings
Announces that the 'King of Kings',
Jehovah, Yaweh, Lord Creator
Would like you as his incubator.
OK, you prayed, you asked a favour –
Some help in staying pure and good
But God, it seems, misunderstood
And politely asks you bear the saviour.
(No need for natural procreation,
He's used divine insemination)."

"So, one, you're not prepared financially,
And two, you've missed your lustful chance.
Your life is now not unsubstantially
More stressful. Joseph looks askance
In your direction – he's suspicious,
Refers to you in crude, lubricious,
Street-Aramaic, scorns your tears...
With time, his jealous chagrin clears,
You scrimp and save for 36
Fraught weeks of numinous gestation,
Compound this with the irritation
Of riding bareback through the sticks
Upon a donkey, listless, wild
And most unfit for one with child..."

"To top it all you must endure
(The consequence of not prebooking),
Delivery amid manure
With rows of bovine eyes all looking.
It doesn't stop there either, friends –
Poor Mary's ill luck never ends.
Her son turns out a firebrand
Who never lends his dad a hand
At work. He sees himself as higher
Than mundane work, feels nails and saws
And joining shelving, whittling doors,
Malapropos for a messiah
And hangs out with his unwashed clique
Of followers and wows the meek."

"How best to honour such a life,
Beset by grief from ears to ankles?
A press-ganged mother, shotgun wife,
Yet did she once allow these rankles
To dim her spirits? No! So keeping
Your Christmas cheer locked up and sleeping
Before the clock's ticked round to ten
Offends her memory. Ladies, men,
This is an invite! Neighbours – mine's
The happening place! (Flat 85)
If you conspire to not arrive
'Til dawn you'll miss the food and wines
More fit for laird or potentate.
(No dress-code. Come from six... 'til late)."

Chapter 3

Wherein our hero is attired and startled

One final, flourish – reckless, thrilling
Is what I crave. I know it's wrong
To leave posterity the billing
But life – each man's short doleful song
(A minor chord or two, faint strumming
All ending in chaotic drumming)
Should not diminish in a swamp
Of assonance, but with a romp,
A crashing jubilant finale.
The forms of these concluding joys
Are many: some want bedroom toys,
Some holidays in Greece or Bali,
While others crave for *Haute Cuisine*
Before they vanish from the scene.

The perk of seeing all too plainly
That self-extinction's just around
The next bend on my life's ungainly
Dual carriageway is that the Pound
Has ceased to be a thing for saving.
I'm free to satisfy each craving
For Prada shoes, Armani suits
Versace shirts and Gucci boots.
I've even boosted up my wealth
With unsecured, high-interest credit.
I must confess I chose to edit
My details on the form – 'rude health'
I wrote and then resolved to shop
Quite literally until I drop.

I shaved and scrupulously clipped
My sideburns, moisturised each cheek,
Flossed keenly, gargled mouthwash, stripped
And showered, scrubbed, drip-dried, and slipped
My outfit on, lime chords, grey jacket,
There, burning at my breast: a *packet*
(Three grand, creatively, I'd wangled
From Lloyds). My hair was lank and tangled
Like sodden bindweed, I fetched comb
And Brylcreem, filled my haversack:
At Swim-Two-Birds in paperback
(Essential for the journey home)
My mackintosh in case of rain,
And lunch – Roquefort on Multigrain.

Now, Oxford Street is not for purists,
It's not the place for finest shopping.
Its pavements swarm with dawdling tourists
In anoraks, inanely bopping
In day-glow yellows, greens and reds.
Their portly frames and gawping heads
Obstruct all native folk like me
From passing free from A to B.
From Marble Arch and right on through
Past Selfridges and Oxford Circus
A Londoner will go berserk as
He's forced to bite his lip and queue
With shopaholics from all nations
And all their wild gesticulations.

I've been detained by Spaniards screeching
With questions like, "Excuse me, where
Is Windsor castle?" Danes beseeching,
"How can I find Lye-Sess-Ter-Square?"
I feel a merciless frustration
When asked "Where's Big Ben Metro Station?"
And cannot curb a sense of scorn
When met with "Hey, is this Whole Borne?"
It seems the Queen's official seat is
A palace that's pronounced to rhyme
With "trucking ham" (you think that I'm
Too sensitive? That I should treat this
As quaint and not so soul-destroying?
But Reader! It's just *so annoying!*)

The ideal mode of self-protection
Against these questions' blunt inanity –
Assume an alien inflection
And save your shopping-time and sanity:
I'll scare off Dustin from El Paso
With my imposing Polish Basso –
I glare and blurt "przepraszam pana!"
In such a frenzied, guttural manner
That rapidly he'll gulp, retreat
(With seven bags from Harrods' Sale,
And little Casey on his tail),
To some more populated street
Where, free of foreign-tongued vexation,
They find the Tourist Information.

I passed through splendid thoroughfares
Past vast museums, red brick mews,
Past shifty men with shifty wares,
iPods for knock-down prices, shoes
That tumbled "off a passing lorry"
And trestle tables piled with sorry
Collections of fake DVDs,
Then crowds of giggling Japanese
Entranced by flat-capped vendors selling
Faux-fragrances like KC One
(By Kelvin Cline), Eve Saint Laurent,
And Channel 5 (please note the spelling!)
As you'd expect, I left this gaggle
To sniff and point and gaily haggle.

Esteemed Reader, what suits me best,
The haunt of all discerning men,
Is found a little further west;
The King's Road's gloss, Sloane Square, South Ken –
Where shops are sanitary, spacious,
And staff are educated, gracious.
Well-versed in every new-born trend,
They don't nag clientele to spend.
When browsing rails where, close and tangible,
Hang clothes so delicately made
In cashmere, leather, chiffon, suede,
My self-restraint grows faint and frangible.
A bit like Stendhal with a painting,
A well-made shirt can start me fainting.

Motht cherished Reader, I am back,
Tith 'Montheigneur The Great Omnithient'.
I fear our hero'th veered off track,
Can hardly jutht remain tho retithent!
Thith ithn't jutht a harmleth prank,
What he'th done ith defraud a bank.
Lloydth thertainly won't find it funny –
They're motht protective of their money,
And, Reader, one way or another
They'll make thure that they get it back.
Thome thucker'th got to take the flack
(All my conthernth are for hith brother).
All bank'th are run by martinet'th
Who thpit blood over unpaid debt'th!

So, Onward! To the first boutique,
A shoe shop, "Chez Antonio".
Where every pair is quite unique
And where royalty and stars all go
To kit their feet in the latest vogue
Whether sandal, kitten-heel or brogue,
A trendy pair of moccasins
Cut from exotic creature's skins,
Stilettos, 'little stilts', to give
Those shoes their proper name, although
The pairs sold by Antonio
Need not use the diminutive:
So high they add a foot in height,
So dear no bank will underwrite.

The pair I wanted for myself,
After a joyous long peruse,
Were on a lofty copper shelf
And were more Desert Boots than shoes.
I risk now being misconstrued!
This nomenclature can allude
To rough-hewn uppers, pseudo-suede,
Crepe soles and heels all cheaply made,
Then fastened gracelessly together
With weak adhesive glue bathetically...
And nothing like my pair, aesthetically:
Hand-cut from tender, supple leather
From rare blue-blooded, day-old foals,
And stitched to varnished oak-wood soles.

At last, thank God, I found my size.
True union of foot and boot.
Relieved, I paid amid loud sighs
And turned attention to the suit
My host wore with such bold panache.
"I must say... you cut quite a dash...
Your suit? Erm... I don't mean to pry,
It's just it's really caught my eye."
"No problem, boss, don't think I mind.
A compliment ain't so offensive."
He grinned, though seemed a little pensive.
"Boss, suits like these are hard to find."
His tone turned serious, judicial,
"The shop is kind of unofficial.

"And if I let on, tell you where
It is, it might just land us both
In trouble." "I'll keep shtum, I swear!"
"And you must take a solemn oath,
To keep this well beneath your hat.
Now, tell me, Boss, can you do that?"
He said, his voice now hushed and husky.
"Antonio, now, you can trust me."
I said, and sensed his relaxation.
He slyly winked, bade me draw closer,
"This operation's not quite kosher,"
He said. "And to avoid taxation
The premises are well sequestered
Beneath my shop. Now come", he gestured.

So then I followed him out back,
Around the till, past countless pairs
Of loafers all piled in a stack,
Then down a narrow flight of stairs
With nauseating twists and curves
Unsettling for my fragile nerves.
At last we reached some solid ground
And I began to look around
But couldn't see much of the room
Or make out anything within it.
Antonio said, "Wait a minute",
A light bulb flickered in the gloom.
Soon all the basement was ablaze.
My eyes adjusted to the haze.

My first reactions once full-sighted
Were spasms of unbridled fear.
As mentioned, nerves have always blighted
My daily life, but, good grief! Here
My anxiousness reached overdrive...
How on God's earth would I survive
This dark, horrific, monstrous ghoul
Whose shadow towered up the wall
For several dark atrocious metres?
I felt for me and my new mate
Antonio – it seemed our fate
Was that this beast would slay and eat us!
Unless Antonio had planned it –
Was he some sort of voodoo bandit?

Perhaps he'd lured me to his basement –
The bait (he'd hooked me): fancy clothes –
To perpetrate some gross abasement,
Like torture, branding and... heaven knows?
Was I, blind with consumer zeal,
Enticed down here to be a meal
For Antonio's mutated son,
Who scrambles human flesh for fun?
My own flesh had now got much colder:
Such gruesome thoughts flashed through my mind.
I heard a crackle from behind,
Felt something clammy clasp my shoulder:
"Hey boss, are you feeling okay?
You don't look in too good a way."

We know our man'th a nervouth fool,
And, Reader, it'th ath you deduthed:
The "beatht" projected on the wall
Wath the shadow he himthelf produced.
Thometime'th I wonder (you must too)
Quite how our hero make'th it through
A thingle day in London Town
Without completely breaking down.
Tho don't be thtartled if he thkipth
A patch of narrative and rushes
Right patht thith thcene to thpare hith blushes.
I bet inthtead he blithely quipth
"It wath a real Aladdin'th cave..."
Poor chap, he'th really not too brave.

It was a cave fit for Aladdin,
With clothing here the dazzling treasury.
Antonio, now neatly clad in
An apron, here began to measure me
And sketch my shapely details down in
His notebook. After waves of frowning,
He poked my ribs, and flailed his arms
"All done", he said, and rubbed his palms.
"Your chest, Boss, is a forty-two,
And Boss, your waist, now hang on, wait,
I make your waist a thirty-eight.
OK, does that sound right to you?"
There's nothing worse than clothes too tight,
So, glum, I said, "that sounds just right".

Admittedly it's been a while
Since I last purchased clothes anew
But the chinos (taupe, of casual style),
I swear, were waist size thirty-two
(They came – reduced – from BHS).
Now surely I *should* measure less,
And, after all, degenerate
Is what I should do, and the weight
Should now be falling pound by pound
(Or, rather, stone by sickly stone).
And I should now be skin and bone!
As for the swollen girth around
My chest, I'm sure it wasn't more,
In inches, than a thirty-four!

I guess one lets one's figure go:
One smokes too much and thus reneges
On promises made long ago
(I.e. cut down on cheese, fried eggs
Or sausage breakfasts, keep the boozing
To once a week), but, when you're losing,
It's hard to keep yourself so chipper!
When every day you're doomed, slip a
Predestined lap behind, in spite of
Assorted diets or exercise
Or healthy regimens... one sighs,
And finds that one begins to write off
One's case of flesh and what's within it
When one's sure that no future's in it.

I know this melancholy musing
Just draws me closer to the brink.
It serves no good and is just using
Up my resolve. I will not sink
Into the bleak, macabre morass
Of bitterness – it's just so crass.
A sadsack's just so unattractive!
And I know just how I *should* act: live
My last allotted slice of time
Ignoring the increasing tightness
Inside my chest, I'll move with lightness
And joy. To brood would be a crime.
So what! I've got a little fatter,
Essentially it doesn't matter.

So, with my mood both pepped and bucked up,
My mind becalmed and reconfigured,
Dear Reader, it was time I plucked up
My selfhood's flesh and bone and slithered
(Or more like squeezed) inside a suit.
My host displayed a rare, astute
Awareness of my taste (some feat!):
"This velvet number's pretty sweet.
Why don't you try it on for size?"
"You're right, it does posses an air
Of class, it's just what I would wear.
Antonio, avert your eyes."
Before he'd time to count a quinary
I'd dressed myself in purple finery.

"A great choice, Tony, I commend you!
Now, payment... what do you propose?"
"Boss, though that really does depend, you
Don't have the cash now, I suppose?
It's just that... as I've said already..."
"Then say no more, your cash is ready!"
I didn't need to ask a sum,
Just licked my forefinger and thumb
Excitedly with keen saliva,
Then transferred twenties, tenners, ponies
From my vibrating hands to Tony's.
Upon one crumpled, dog-eared fiver
Atop the pile, in soggy crown,
The queen suppressed her stoic frown.

I took Antonio aback
With all the cash now in his hands.
The zenith of this sterling stack
Was far beyond his wildest plans.
"You're far too kind, Boss, this is silly!
You can't spend money willy-nilly,
A grand's an economic coup
For me, but it would bankrupt you...
My shop's clandestine, I'm a crook,
In that sense, and I *am* possessive
With money but won't make excessive
Financial gain from friends. Now look,
Take half this back so you can spend free
Another day... or you'll offend me."

As Tony's protestations grew
More vocal, my resistance swelled,
Grew stiffer, like a stubborn glue
Of principle, had me compelled
To make him take the lot. Unbending,
I felt no reticence in spending
When I considered that the loan
Was Lloyd's money and not my own
(But... I misrepresent myself!
My trumpet's not too often blown
But, Reader, I will have it known
That issues of financial wealth
Were secondary here. You see,
I liked him – he'd been good to me).

By this point his exasperation
Was chronic. All his tearful twittering
Deserved a decent explanation:
"The reason for my flippant frittering
Of all this precious cash away
Is... this might be the final day
In which I'm free to blithely spend
Before I meet my mortal end.
Dear Tony, please try, if you can,
To humour me. Now take my gift.
You wouldn't want to cause a rift
With an eccentric dying man...
Oh God, don't cry now! Take this tissue...
I didn't want to raise this issue!"

"But when you begged and genuflected
I felt bound to enlighten you..."
"But Boss! How sad! How unexpected!
It's just too much... it can't be true!"
And, Reader, so it came to pass:
The two of us shared glass on glass
Of frothy goodness deep inside
The vaults of next door's Duchamp's Bride.
There flowed the long and slurry trails
Of our life stories (love/sex lives,
Our schooling, Tony's seven ex-wives,
Fellini's films, the role of males
In our postmodern world, the army,
The literature of Murakami).

We parted, late, the best of friends,
My raiments were by now quite crumpled.
I'd bought the drinks to make amends
(He was too hammered to have rumbled)
For the five-hundred quid that he'd
Sworn vehemently he didn't need.
My diagnosis was outlined,
I counselled him to pay no mind –
Death picks us off like ripened fruits,
Whether quince, pear, Ugli, Golden Delicious,
Or kumquat, he is so capricious,
He takes us when he feels it suits –
That life throws mud into one's eye
And ours is not to question why.

I made him promise, though, before
He staggered off his separate way,
That he'd come knocking at my door
And join the guests on Christmas day.
I took his business card detailing
His number, while, against a railing,
He leant, unzipped, went on to drain
His bladder of all Castlemaine.
"Ciao boss, I've had a lovely night.
I hate goodbyes... they're all such fuss..."
With that he leapt onto a bus
And swiftly hurtled out of sight
In clouds of bilious, chugging red.
I woke next morning, ill, in bed.

Oh when will our young hero learn,
Dear Reader, that he mutht take care –
That alcohol will only burn
Up hith inthide'th? – I'd pull my hair
Out in exathperated thtrandth
If I pothethed a pair of handth
(And thomething that the more athtute
Of you will note: a head, hirthute).
I lack a body'th phythicality,
And I've no tholid concrete form,
No heart and lungth to keep en forme,
No concrete tangible reality,
Tho all hith vain, impulthive actionth
Jutht aggravate me through abththractionth.

Chapter 4

Wherein our hero meets an eccentric lady

December: frozen drainage sluices
Are symptomatic in my block.
South London's frantic, active juices
Are petrified in winter shock.
The silver arc of precious sun
Feels like it's only just begun
Its faint parabola of light –
At 4pm it leaves our sight.
And now the mournful starless firmament
Shifts rapidly in its deep hue –
First dusky mauve then navy blue
Then inky black – night's almost permanent.
All eyes one meets are dull, dejected,
Morose and seasonally affected.

A real "disorder", SAD,
Not some complaint slyly concocted
By some astute drug company,
Then avariciously adopted
By all of us, each blindly keening
For truth, some scientific meaning,
Or pharmaceuticals to chew
To stop us feeling wintry blue.
But we are creatures of extremes,
We'll protest outside any shops
That stock their shelves with GM crops,
And Karloff carrots haunt our dreams.
We'll meddle with the human brain,
But won't dare touch our precious grain.

The spindly skeletons of oak,
Their frozen shapes wizened and hoary,
Are nude without their leafy cloak,
The Rye's own bleak *momenti mori*.
The absence of all sprightly fauna
Reminds me of what's round the corner.
The air is redolent of bonfires
And makes one think of funeral pyres.
My mood was low, my heaving chest
Encased a heart that lacked vitality,
Quite overwhelmed by its mortality.
But then I saw his scarlet breast –
The Robin for whom there's no reason
Why winter is the bleakest season.

No darkling thrush, no nightingale,
No light-winged Dryad of the trees,
No skylark winging over dale,
Emitting doleful melodies,
No sparrow – favourite of Catullus –
To thrill, to trill, to coo and lull us,
Young poetasters, to pen lyrics,
Or madrigals and panegyrics
On all things feathered, all things winged.
This was no muse, no bardic bird,
But a stoic Robin that I heard.
He scuttled, sang, his small beak ringed
By morning mist that screened his head –
A spectral patch of floating red.

A minuscule electric fire
With all the vigour of young sprites,
He flitted low then billowed higher,
A beacon outside Donjong Heights.
And with each bold, ebullient dart,
The Robin stirred my faulty heart,
And while he danced before my eyes
I felt my spirit galvanise.
This all became an allegory:
The leaden winter's misty stillness
Here represented my own illness.
The bird played *my* part in the story;
He waved two fingers at the gods
Who'd dealt us both such rotten odds.

Though birds are birds and men are men,
Anthropomorphism's inane –
I hold my hands up (guilty!) – then
That bird was truly transmundane
(Before you cry in baffled chorus,
According to my old thesaurus:
The Latin root of 'trans' – 'beyond' –
Prefixing 'mundane' – '*mundus*', '*monde*'...)
He spoke in transcendental song,
And not in words. I should explain:
He lectured from a higher plane
And to describe it would be wrong,
Would not translate the pulchritude,
So my rendition is but crude:

Cheep cheep tweet, trill, cheep tweety tweet!
Trill trill cheep, tweet, trill cheepy cheep!
Life is a funfare, oh life is sweet!
Don't live your life like you're half-asleep!
One day you'll blink, life will be over,
This is what I learnt from the wise old Plover.
Seek out beauty, do all you can,
This is what I learnt from the Tragopan.
Even in hardship, never be cross,
These are the words of the Arctic Tern.
Every day gives us lessons to learn,
These are the words of the Albatross.
Life only comes once, you can't live it twice,
Listen to the Bird of Paradise!

My body filled with sweet sensations
Of light and energy and quickness.
I felt excited palpitations,
Despite my slow heart's languid sickness!
I snatched my scrawled inventory,
The list of each picked invitee:
Ex-academic, John J. Johnson,
Lord Byron, governed by *his* Johnson,
Young Tyrone, DJ, reprobate,
Hylie the fair-skinned Rasta-Queen
(I planned a vegan, pasta, bean
Nut loaf to make her salivate),
My brother to protect the fort,
Antonio my new cohort.

I felt revived, enthusiastic,
Dressed clumsily in shirt and jeans.
With eager gestures, vaguely spastic,
I donned my coat, felt full of beans,
And with a pink soirée request
Prepared for each suggested guest
Who lived nearby in the vicinity
Of Donjong Heights, the ill-matched trinity
Of John J. Johnson, Hylie, Tyrone
(Lord Byron lives in Crystal Palace,
I'd find him though, hands round a chalice
Of Liebfraumilch or Côtes du Rhône
Inside the Gibbon's Head with John,
Intoxicated, prattling on...),

I strode into the corridor.
I don't know what you'll think of me
But, as I glanced back through the door,
I swear the Robin winked at me.
First on my list: my next-door neighbour,
Tyrone, whose voluble behaviour,
A one man, all-night Dub Selecta,
Had pained and irked the common recta
Of us good tenants. But today
I was noble and magnanimous,
Forgiving of nocturnal fuss –
I'm sure he's pleasant, in his way.
Beyond his door (no. 89)
I heard an ominous bassline.

Two hundred ragged beats-per-minute –
The yapping of a cyborg dog –
A tune with no real music in it
Accompanied the toxic fog
Of prime and high-grade sinsemilla
The door let out, and I felt ill, a
Vague dizziness engulfed me, I
Knocked anyway, and, meekly, "Hi",
Fell out my mouth. The vile polyphony
(Monotonous, the drums kept rumbling,
No let-up in the bassline's grumbling)
Felt like the inverse of epiphany –
A malediction capped at source
Transmuted into stereo force.

Sage Bertrand Russell, he, no less
(And seconded by Ted Adorno),
Declared the modern world a mess,
But not because of guns or porno.
They said the *music* everywhere
Leaves man no calm in which to stare
Attentively into the mind,
That all this pop leaves us quite blind
(Or deaf) to issues more profound.
I'm not sure music's such a villain
(I like the Pogues, Smiths, pre-God Dylan)
But now the manufactured sound
Is one long line of turgid dross:
The Spice Girls, S-Club, Take That, Bros.

I knocked a second time: more vehement,
More forceful, both fists rapped the wood.
I hollered something incoherent,
(*Saaf Londonese*, as best I could)
Until the speakers crackled and popped
And finally the music stopped.
"Who is it? If you're here for weed,
I'm out!" "Tyrone, it's you I need.
It's me, your neighbour, from next door"
"Oh... um", I guess he thought about it
For a sec' or two, then shouted out, "It...
It's you, man, innit? From next door?
You want me crank the music up?"
"No! Listen, Tyrone, open up!

I've got an invite, it's for you"
"An *invitation*, what d'you mean?"
"Well, see, I'm putting on a do"
I was polite, I was saccharine
In my civility. "A rave?"
Here I resolved that I'd behave
As any neighbour should, "Not quite,
A dinner party, Christmas night."
A slit opened, the door ajar,
His eye (huge pupil, burst red vein)
Blinked indolently with disdain.
"This all sounds a bit la-de-dah"
"But it will be a gourmet feast"
"I 'spose you'll 'ave some booze, at least?"

"Yes plenty – Beaujolais, Merlot,
Chianti, Grappa – the whole hog!"
"You what, man? How about some Strongbow?
And will you have a chocolate log?"
"Um... oh... Well, OK, and a platter
Of dips, like Tarama Salata,
Tzatziki, Houmous, home-made Coleslaw..."
"Eh?" Tyrone picked a crusty coldsore...
His door creaked open. "Come", he said,
And motioned with a bitten digit
(He's prone to nail-bite, sniffle, fidget
And prod his gushing nose). Instead
Of offering to shake my palm
He grinned and punched me on the arm –

A friendly gesture, so I'm reckoning,
Employed by all the streetwise youth.
I followed Tyrone's mindful beckoning
And saw for the first time the truth,
The chaos of my neighbour's flat.
Dear Reader, now, to tell you that
It was a mess would be to lie.
Not fit for pigs, this was a sty
Of silver foil, unopened mail,
Discoloured undergarments, socks,
And pizza, mouldy, in its box.
The ambience was moist and stale.
Tyrone proffered an upturned crate,
And mumbled, "Take a seat there, mate".

Internally, my neighbour's cel
Once scrutinised from floor to top
Was less the toxomanic hell
More glossy shrine to Hip and Hop.
A sinewy, bejewelled, chocolate brown
And life-size 2Pac grimaced down
From several posters, and from others
Scowled Busta Rhymes, The Jungle Brothers,
Two Ices – Messers Cube and T –
A group shot of the Wu-Tang Clan
With blunts in each hand, to a man,
Snoop Dogg and Dre, amid a sea
Of well-oiled, surgically augmented
Young models, grinned out stoned, demented.

Tyrone was watching me inspect
His Gangsta-Rapping decoration
And felt compelled to interject,
Make clear to me his adoration
Of all these men was intellectual –
He liked their music, nothing sexual
Could possibly, at all, be read in
To this display... he'd "smash my head in"
(And anybody else's too)
If they attempted to suggest
He liked the rapper's bodies best.
For him the only thing to do
If his young manhood was in doubt:
Respond by way of kick or clout.

So, Reader, for your future reference,
In case you ever meet the guy,
Don't question Tyrone's sexual preference –
You'll end up with a blackened eye.
Perhaps he doth protest too much?
Is there a meaning veiled by such
A fierce avowal of his status?
If one, with Freudian apparatus
Directed on his callow mind,
Could probe the depths of his young psyche,
Past fetishes of all things Nike,
What secret longings would one find?
But what you find should stay unknown –
You'd risk your health to tell Tyrone.

"Without intending to disparage
These Hip-Hop dons, they've had their time.
These days what turns me on is Garage,
And 2-step stuff like UK Grime
With tight MC's, and, Tyrone, we know
Of Dizzee, Oxide and Neutrino,
Roll Deep and Wiley, More Fire Crew –
They're prime exponents of this new,
Original, homegrown construction
Of gritty urban vocal flow,
With beats sped up and bass pitched low,
Inspired by Drum 'n' Bass production...
You mix in dirty London slang
And bosh... You've got the whole shebang!"

This was my speech (how well I bluffed!)
Designed to mollify Tyrone.
I must admit I felt quite chuffed,
These things I never knew I'd known
Poured out to eulogise and praise
This latest urban music craze.
"I think you've got a point", he said,
And scratched his freshly-shaven head.
"But Drum 'n' Bass aint dead, and never..."
"I don't mean it will disappear!
Perhaps I didn't make it clear,
One really cannot altogether
Write Jungle off, I wouldn't dare,
But 2-step is its rightful heir."

My neighbour nodded, calm, approving,
Placated by my stirring argument.
So I stepped up the job – removing
His gnarly tough-guy's outer tegument
And any final dubitation
He had about my invitation.
"So what d'you say, my gathering?
It won't be highbrow blathering,
We live in an eclectic age.
The tenants of this tower block
Are hardly a conceited flock,
You'll feel no need to disengage
From friendly chat – and lots of drink.
So come on Tyrone, what do you think?"

I left Tyrone's flat satisfied
That he'd be present at my bash.
His rugged macho front belied
A young man, though a little brash
And over eager with the slap,
Who wasn't such an awful chap.
Next on my list was Hylie's grotto.
She'd pasted to her door the motto:
"I and I and Rastafari
Give universal peace and love",
I gave the door a gentle shove
And stepped inside, but not too far, I
Knew Hylie never locked her door –
Believing it against Jah's law.

And there she sat, with legs contorted
In Lotus pose, right in the centre
Of her front room. My nose reported
Up to my brain a heady scent, a
Degree more pleasant than the stench
At Tyrone's flat – I didn't blench
But here imbibed this heady odour,
Imagined myself in Baroda.
She stayed quite motionless, entranced,
Unbothered by her ginger Tom
Who pawed her. She sustained her Om
A minute more before she glanced
Towards me with her chartreuse eyes
That showed no flicker of surprise.

"Hi, sorry for the brief delay...
I really mustn't interrupt
A meditative state halfway –
Bad for the chakras, too abrupt."
She rearranged her matted hair.
I thought of Murphy and his chair,
But checked this thought, it was unkind;
"Oh no! Don't worry, I don't mind.
Was it a good, erm... meditate?"
"It went OK, but it's a strain
Accessing the ninth Astral Plane."
"The ninth? I've only heard of eight."
Oh no, at last count fifty-four,
But there could well be several more."

Tom nudged her bare foot with his head,
With shrill belligerence he mewed.
"Oh Tomcat's waiting to be fed!
Why don't you join us two for food?"
She asked me. "Love to" I replied.
"Today it's soya, lightly fried
In pine oil with a peanut sauce,
You're not allergic?" "No, of course
I'm not. It sounds, well... quite divine!"
"I'd say it's Tomcat's favourite food"
Now obdurate, on cue he mewed –
A frantic, starving, feline whine.
I wished this Nouveau Hip Cuisine
Be full of blushful Hippocrene.

"Now, you two introduce yourselves.
I'm sure you'll get on really well...
No, Tom! Not on my Tarot shelves..."
"If you need help just give a yell."
She vanished through a wall of beads
That rustled like metallic reeds.
I turned my interest to the feline
Who'd made the tentative short b-line
Towards my foreign-smelling feet
And sniffed, with scrupulous attention,
And airs of subtle condescension,
To check my aura: was it sweet?
Or were the vibes that I emitted
Ones Tom felt shouldn't be admitted?

Soon sizzling sounds and chopping bangs,
The odd dropped tin, the odd curt missive
('Oh fuck, that's hot!") caused hungry pangs.
And I felt wrong – far too dismissive,
And far too keen to overlook
What Hylie had proposed to cook
In such a brash and ready fashion
Without due culinary compassion.
My stomach growled in loud accord
With Tom's, which, though an octave higher,
Exhibited the same desire,
An equal salivating chord
For what our stomachs sensed would be
A gastronomic symphony.

There's no more powerful device
For stirring up one's wits than food:
The steaming scent of lemon rice,
Plump meatballs being deeply stewed,
Bouquet of molten Camembert,
Espresso's rich and heady air,
The smell of fresh bread in mid-bake...
A dormant hunger, once awake,
Needs to be satisfied *tout suite*
Or else one's belly will revolt
With rumblings and the odd sharp jolt –
Insistent on its veg or meat.
To my relief my host returned,
Her pinkie finger slightly burned.

"Hey you two boys, the waiting's over!"
She carried nimbly, with great calm,
As graceful as the great Pavlova,
Three metal bowls on each thin arm.
"Where should I sit?" "Oh, where you please,
I find it best cross-legged, with knees –
The right for Soya, left for rice –
Around my bowls, a natural vice."
"I see, dear Hylie, though I fear
I'm not so able at contortion.
I'll take the sensible precaution
And, boringly, *kneel* down right here."
It won't have caught you unawares,
Dear Reader: Hylie had no chairs.

Appropriately, on four feet –
In keeping with my metric form –
Tom joined my host and I to eat.
Apparently it was the norm
That mistress here would dine with cat:
I couldn't mock or poke fun at
Such human/feline *egalité*
With mean *anthropocentralité*.
His tongue, a fibrous worm of pink,
Imbibed the Soya with such zeal –
Before I'd half consumed my meal
He'd slunk away (a well-fed slink)
Gave out a lazy caterwaul,
Waited for Morpheus to call...

Once rice was finished, Soya chewed,
Bowls stacked like metal Matrioshki,
Our guts engaged to process food
And rumbled satisfaction softly.
As Hylie hummed a thank-you mantra,
I felt the perfect way to thank her
For all the food, so pure and hearty,
Would be: invite her to my party.
(And after all that was the plan –
The reason why I paid this visit)
"You know it's Christmas soon" "Oh, is it?"
"It is, and though no Christian man
I want to somehow celebrate
With all the folk of our estate

"A gathering of disparate minds
Who, by some act of luck or chance,
Exist in Donjong Heights' confines,
Drawn here by fate's mysterious dance."
"Wow, that sounds far out, I'll be there.
When is it?" "Christmas night." "Oh yeah –
I use a pagan calendar...
I'm not sure what the big dates are.
My months start with each newborn moon,
Don't have the Roman nomenclature
That's of unnatural manufacture.
For all I know we're now in June!"
"Well, one thing that you should remember
Is, Christmas falls in late December...

"To be exact: the twenty-fifth."
"Yeah, I'll be there, it sounds well irie.
So, how about we share a spliff?
I've got some hash that's pretty fiery."
As she had been the model host,
I thought, 'why not a herbal toast
To thank Jah for the rice and soya?'
I'd disregard the paranoia
I've got from smoking down the years.
A dying person shouldn't shirk
From pleasure. "It's a blend of Turk-
Ish Black and Magic from Tangiers.
It gives a cosy mellow high
And doesn't leave the throat too dry."

Now Hylie fetched a metal tin
(Emblazoned with a large hemp leaf
Of bright fluorescent green), therein,
Beyond the smoker's leitmotif,
A lump of hash, a tiny coal
That she, with dextrous hand-control,
Soon warmed and crumbled into paper.
I caught the vaguely sickly vapour:
It swirled in pungent rivulets
Around the room, caressed the ceiling,
Induced in me a slothful feeling.
Then Hylie beamed, "all done, now let's
Both smoke, kick back, relax, feel free,
Inhale the cosmic energy!"

I saw her as a youthful sibyl –
Her yogic pose, her blurry eyes –
As if residing in an idyll
Of fluffy moons and liquid skies
Of talking cats and dancing trees
All ruled by louche, stoned deities.
She passed the joint for me to toke,
I filled my feeble lungs with smoke
But forthwith, like a gushing tap,
Expelled it all with spluttering zest
(Avoiding a protruding breast)
And covered Hylie's purple lap...
"Oh how embarrassing, I'm sorry!"
Hylie implored me not to worry.

"Why don't you try another puff?
It does possess a certain kick.
At first this stuff's a little rough,
You'll cough a bit, but won't be sick
Again." I rasped and sucked and toiled
With spliff, while Hylie, robes now soiled
With specks of Soya (and her face
Quite sticky), skipped off to replace
Her clothes and let the old ones soak
In mint and tea-tree oil Ecover.
I did my best to breathe, recover
My self-control and tried to choke
The urge to wretch and re-anoint
The floor... then turned back to the joint...

Then, after three aborted tries
I got the trick, began inhaling
And soon felt tightness round my eyes.
The patterned wallpaper detailing
Rosebuds and creepers on the climb
Communicated such sublime
And subtle pleasures, moving, luminous,
I found the whole sensation numinous.
Delightful sounds bled through the mist –
The cat's mellifluous light purrs,
As soft as velveteen-lined furs,
Caressed my soul and softly kissed
A point within my buzzing brain
Like gentle hypnogogic rain.

Tho firtht he'th tipthy with a tailor
And now indulgeth in the weed.
Oh! Mutht I shout through a loud hailer?
Why will our hero not take heed
Of all the counthel doctor gave him?
I fear the warningth will not thave him
From an untimely painful grave
If he continueth to behave
Like thith quite thtupid, hedonithtic
And indethtructable young man.
With fragile heart the wortht one can
Engage in ith thith vile, thadithtic
And noxious thtuff. He'll only thpeed up
Hith death by thucking all thith weed up!

I passed through castles, vast, palatial,
Elysian fields and sapphire oceans.
Perceptions – time, substance and spatial –
Were blurred and adumbrated notions.
My hearing, taste, smell, touch and sight
Reached their collective sensual height,
United in a glowing nexus
Condensed behind my solar plexus.
Soon Reggae skanks began to pulse
From speakers that were well concealed,
My body lurched, convulsed and reeled
With ecstasy. A vague impulse,
Both frivolous and quite profound,
Compelled my feet to prance around.

Now dancing isn't what I'd call
My forte – and that's understated.
I shunned my graduation ball
For fear of being obligated
To jig and twist and spin and thrust.
My four limp limbs get wanderlust
And slither off their separate way –
Four adders after different prey.
And on a level more abstruse:
Except for Sufis whirling, spiritual,
Most dancing's just a mating ritual
Engaged in by the crass and loose.
I'd like to think my conversations
Are more seductive than gyrations.

Despite the purely social sense,
On which my views are crystal clear
(All lewd, lascivious pretence,
Excuse to fumble, grope and leer),
There is, of course, as with all arts,
A higher form to touch our hearts
And lofty intellectual minds.
Instead of vulgar bumps and grinds
And other titillating poses:
The lithe conveyance of emotion –
The ballerina's locomotion
Of limbs provides a heightened gnosis
And vivifies the soul much more
Than shufflings on a disco floor.

Quite how I got my swaying mass
To stand back upright I'm not sure
(My every molecule, *en masse*,
Propelled me up across the floor).
With feet as nimble as ham shanks
And legs as pliable as planks
Of obstinately solid cedar
The music swept me up like Leda
By that colossal, lustful swan.
I thought about "On Wine and Hashish"
By Baudelaire, felt wild and raffish,
Until, without fresh clothing on,
My host, with wrists and ankles bangled,
Returned on naked legs that jangled.

I stood agog and puzzled as
She pranced towards me with a grin,
Carefree in nudity, whereas
I, fully clothed, felt from within
A surge of bashfulness, red-hot,
Each cheek burned like a solar spot
Upon my startled face. She span
With arms outstretched – a turbine fan
Of naked woman. Though unrest
Rushed all through me in boiling ripples
I had to stare: her carmine nipples
On pyramidal mounds of breast,
Below, a woolly ginger tangle,
Her fiery pubic love triangle.

She danced. Her limbs all clinked like coins
In pockets, or a bunch of keys
(Uneasy stirrings in my loins,
A failing strength about my knees –
The trembling might of cookie dough).
I strove to find some droll *bon mots*
(A desperate, very un-Lawrentian
Vain scramble to deflect attention):
"Oh, Hylie! What a grand erection!
 Oh no... I mean... quel parapraxis!
Rotating on your shoeless axis
With such smooth grace... such sweet perfection,
Just like a young, redhead Bardot...
Is that the time? Oh! I should go... "

"So soon! Why don't you stay awhile?
We could perform a mystic rite
In which our bodies, bare, fusile,
With primal symmetry, unite
And share, together, in the bliss
Of their communal nakedness."
I stood stock still in my position
(But was it fear or indecision
That kept me rooted to the floor?)
I could either succumb and undress,
Join my unorthodox seductress,
Or else, behind me was the door –
I could confer my invitation,
Then flee her lusty gurgitation.

Chapter 5

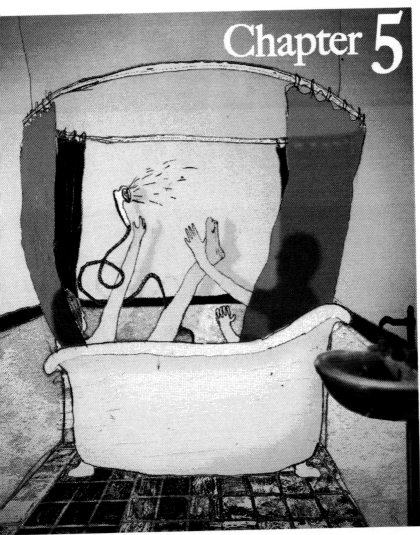

Wherein our hero writes a letter

How strange an image or a fraction
Of past emotion is suggested
By some more current simulacrum
Of something one's mind once invested
To memory's tenuous protection
In order that its sharp perfection
Is kept intact and somehow vital.
How odd that this psychic requital
Is sparked off by a mundane incident
In present conscious life, prosaic
But that our frontal lobe's mosaic
Of spongy cells translates as pertinent –
A game of whispers in Chinese
Where "s'il vous plait" ends up as "please".

Now I recall one splendid night
With Catherine, where we sh`ared a meal,
Clandestine, in the candlelight
(In case Chester, with prurient zeal,
Should infiltrate), and at which wine
(A citrus-tinged, dry '99
Chateauneuf du Pape) was swallowed
With great alacrity. I wallowed
For hours in her vast sapphire eyes
(I know – a corny, crass, pubescent
Cliché, forgive me) effervescent,
Like lakes reflecting starry skies
At dusk on a fine summer's eve
As day takes its begrudging leave.

We ate first melon, then fresh bream,
And followed that with sticky toffee
Puddings swathed in buttercream,
Then cheeses, cups of Irish coffee –
Which Catherine found a bit too much.
The bill was paid (our method Dutch).
With bellies full, heads light, we walked
On Peckham's verdant Rye and talked
Of wrestling brothers, singing sisters
(Cat's sister Esther had a show
Just opened at the ENO).
Cat walked in bare feet (new shoes, blisters)
And by the time we made it home
Her painted toes were flecked with loam.

What followed, Reader, is the crux
Of all of this; the root of my
Note on the sudden inward flux
Of scenes that flood mind's cool eye
(For aeons hibernating, latent
They graphically recur as blatant
Bright signposts to emotions deep
That have been buried, fast asleep).
I took it as my job to launder
Cat's soft, unsanitary paws,
Climbed in the bathtub, on all fours.
My sweetheart, though, was wont to maunder,
Due, in no meagre part, I think,
To all the wine she'd had to drink.

The two of us somehow conspired
(Or was it all premeditated?
It seems my memory's too mired
In what this scene precipitated
To give a wholly truthful chronicle),
With machinations wild and comical,
The shower hose out of control,
(Again, the work of alcohol)
While ardently removing from
Cat's feet all vestiges of dirt,
To soak her charming linen skirt.
"How apt!" she giggled with aplomb,
Her rapture building to a swoon
Of mirth, "I bought it at *Monsoon!*"

I played some background tunes (Thelonius
Monk's 'Round Midnight'), sat down, smoking,
When Catherine, hardly parsimonious
With soap and water, joined me, soaking
But well-refreshed after an hour
Of thorough preening in the shower.
She'd lost her dress, found no towel,
Looked sensuous as a Rimbaud vowel.
And this is where my mind's eye rests
It's avid gaze: hips serpentine,
Neck of a shogun's concubine,
Thin, hairless arms, two modest breasts
Damp strands of hair across her eyes,
The muscles twitching in her thighs.

So, back to Hylie, Reader, wouldn't
You like to know how things transpired?
Did I? Didn't I? Well... I couldn't.
As passion's blowtorch wildly fired
And burned a hole right through my crotch
A stirring image came to scotch
And slam and double-bolt the door
On any chance of sweet amour.
For all of half a splintered second,
As if one frame cut from a reel,
I saw an image quite surreal,
Portentous, mystical and fecund:
As Hylie span with rugged grace
I saw upon her Catherine's face.

A room for eating, thleeping, shaving;
A bed, two chairth, a lamp, a dethk,
At which our hero'th now behaving
Motht thtrangely, thitting thculpturethque
(Like Rodin'th thinker but with leth
Calm majethty, more gaunt distreth).
Hith eye'th are hardly open now,
Hith fingerth bitten, hith furrowed brow
He'th thcratched tho much that it'th now painful.
He ripth the paper from the pad,
"My letter writing'th really bad!"
He moanth, then with one latht dithdainful
Glanthe down at hith thcrunched-up creation,
Expelth it by defenethtration.

"I mutht improve. It mutht be crithp,
And luthid, humble and poetic"
He thayth out loud (without the lithp),
"...and heartfelt, frank, apologetic
And not tho overdone and florid
To make her think thome raging, torrid,
Thychotic mind or cocky tyro
Hath got exthited with a Biro.
I will not thleep 'til I've done better!"
With that, for the ninth time tonight,
He hunkerth down and thtartth to write
Thith vain impassioned 'thorry' letter
To Catherine, who he feelth he mutht
Win back before he bite'th the dutht:

"I know it is no use me starting
This letter as if we're old friends.
The sullied nature of our parting
Exists as fact. To make amends
In some small way for that debacle
Is all I want. I know no sparkle
Of love will likely shine again
Between us, and to entertain
A hope that we may even share
The same room, civil conversations
Since my repugnant depravations
Is more than I should dare to dare.
So now, that you continue reading
Is all I'm humbly, meekly pleading."

"I am not a fighting man. I
Have neither brawn nor good technique
And all too readily I cry
And tremble. Once a fit of pique
Consumed me – just once I must stress.
A frenzy I could not suppress
Was generated by a fear
Of losing something I held dear.
A mother shrew will fight a rhino,
A spaniel will attack a lynx
If it – the smaller mammal – thinks
Its young are threatened. And now I know
These touching kamikaze missions
Are born from love without conditions."

"My metaphor, I know, has flaws.
Our bond was ardour, not parental.
But all the same, it underscores,
In its own way, my fundamental
Contention – if you'd just believe it.
My violence: could you not perceive it
As the misplaced, excess product of
A thorough, honest, desperate love?
Perhaps you haven't read this far
And this sad note's been set aflame –
These actions, Cat, I would not blame.
If not, and by some chance you are
Still there, no doubt in indignation,
I must impart some information:"

"I do this with a heavy heart –
Ah, Catherine, if you only knew!
I've doubted deeper than Descartes:
Which course would be the most untrue?
To contact you, apologising,
Beg you to see beyond despising
My memory, and leave it there;
Or, how appropriate, how fair
Would you regard a pained disclosure
Of tragic news? I've agonised
Through sleepless nights and scrutinised
The moral action, like Spinoza...
But... Oh! My dearest Cat, I'm dying...
I've said it now... there's no use lying.

"I've read my Hume, my Kant, I've read
My Wittgenstein and Aristotle
And think... to leave my news unsaid
Would truly be to lose my bottle.
My brand of ethics might be arch
But I've a thirst I've got to parch.
A *secret ache*, a leaden pain,
Pervading body, heart and brain.
The only possible relief
From this dull torpor is, someway,
Get you, by methods fair or fey,
To visit me. I've the belief –
Though you may find this blind faith mad –
That once you saw me you'd be glad."

"That's it, I'm done. I won't impinge
Upon your time for one more second.
I read my own words back and cringe,
Perhaps you will. But if you reckoned
For just a instant, had an inkling
(However small, a meagre sprinkling,
A thimble-full would do) that I
Was not the awful, brutish guy
You took me for, then I implore you
To put me to the test like litmus.
I'm having a soiree at Christmas,
Do come, dear Cat, I beg, before you
Forgo the chance to reunite
Two loving souls – you know I'm right."

A note to readerth: now a change
Of mood, a shift of emphathith
Approacheth uth... but to derange
You with thith clumthy prolepthith
Ith not my motive or intention.
I merely want to draw attention:
The fact ith, from thith moment henthe,
Thith trope employth the prethent tenthe.
If you're not bored, and thtill engaged
And haven't given up by now
Or found thith book ath dull ath Thlough,
If thonnet-hunger'th not athuaged,
Then, kindly Reader, reimmerthe
Your mind in thith mad world of verthe!

So far I've kept this under my
Proverbial beret, but now
My symptoms won't permit the lie
That I'm OK persisting. How
Can I stop my physique parading
The grisly truth that it's abrading,
Degenerating, ebbing, dwindling?
My legs are weak as sodden kindling,
My hands are skeletal and quiver
Ferociously like sculpted jelly;
I suffer cramps in chest and belly
And stabbing twinges in my liver.
My bones shake with the daily thunder
From this Blitzkreig of pain I'm under.

And where does all this torment start?
What is the root of all this pain?
Mon coeur malade, my sickly heart,
That stutters like an aeroplane
With failing engines, one and two,
The third is waning, radar too,
The fuselage drops off in flakes,
I've lost control of all four brakes.
And if a passing gull or sparrow
Peered through the loosening portholes
They'd see, behind the burnt controls,
A pilot, timorous and sallow,
Resigned and in the brace position
Prepared for cardiac collision.

Chapter 6

Wherein our hero enters a public house

So now I limp and teeter off
    Towards the public house in which
    A don and obsolescent toff
Malinger daily, scratch the itch,
Imbibe the hair, relubricate
(And at the same time dehydrate),
With goblets full of 'laughing gas' –
Known better to us laymen as
Stella Artois. The scourge of strips
On Saturday (and Friday) nights;
The catalyst for untold fights
Over women, football, lukewarm chips.
It seems the premium *Bière Belgique*
Breaks fifty noses every week.

Lord B.'s with John J. in a corner.
John smokes a hand-rolled cigarette.
Lord B., as heated as a sauna,
Is holding court: "... videlicet
The Greeks! They need our help, my friend!
Those beastly Turks will spell their end!"
Preoccupied, John's mind's elsewhere.
He stares into the smokey air,
Then back down at the crossword clues
(The Guardian, Page 12) confounded
By "Kerouac or Ginsberg pounded"
(4 letters, starts with B from "Blues" –
"West London team's unhappy song").
I catch his eye from through the throng

Of surly Millwall partisans,
With 'Love' and 'Hate' across their knuckles,
And three off-duty courtesans
In corsets bursting at their buckles.
"A pint of IPA, please, Vicky",
I say. She says that could be tricky:
There's been a problem with the kegs,
And all that's left is foam and dregs.
Instead I opt for London Pride
And with my hands tight round my glass
I, sidling slowly, slowly, pass
The mob and stop at John J.'s side,
Relieved I've trod on no-one's feet.
John bellows a contented "Beat!"

We sit on stools with ragged fringes
Of tapestry and sip our drinks.
"Oh, when our Lordship has his whinges
I just switch off. The fact he thinks
The Greeks are still at war with Turkey
Suggests he has a rather murky
Conception of the current map
Of Europe – poor misguided chap."
John says and quivers with bemusement.
"But anyway, dear boy, yourself:
How is your good old mockney 'elf?
Still finding life a vast amusement?"
"Oh well..." I say, he cuts across me,
"I'm flummoxed... what could ten across be?"

"Don't ask me John, I find those cryptic
Conundrums leave me rather cold.
The language, quirky and elliptic,
Just irks me and I feel quite old
Just looking at them." "What d'you mean?"
"Well, crosswords, John, just aren't my *scene*."
John mumbles something terse about
'The Youth of Britain' to his stout.
"John, keep your Guardian for later.
I wonder whether you might deign
To let me wrack your massive brain."
Now John, the eager educator,
Is all attention, eyes are wide.
The paper's duly cast aside.

"So speak up. Is it literary,
This problem?" "Well, yes, in a way."
"What kind of way?" "Epistolary –
I wrote a letter yesterday..."
"I see, and now you want a critic..."
"No John, it's not your analytic
Abilities I need, it's more
A question of, well... *is* less more
When writing earnest correspondence?"
"Oh dear, oh dear..." John frowns and sips
His Guinness with his shaggy lips.
In paroxysms of despondence
He sighs into the frothy swirl
Atop his drink. "It's for a *girl*..."

"A girl, a woman, what's the difference?
I love her..." "*Love!* Don't use such terms!"
John's eyes, now narrow with indifference,
Have lost their eager glint. He squirms
Upon his barstool, frowns and tuts,
"Women, they're all the same, all sluts.
You think you love them and think they
Love you as well, until one day..."
"... I've heard your tales of woe and treachery
Before, a hundred bitter times...
It's '*Eve, The Mother of All Crimes*'
For you... you won't consider lechery
On your part – clumsy, drunk, uncaring –
To have even the slightest bearing

"On why your marriage failed. John, listen..."
I take my note back, read aloud.
And now John's eyes begin to glisten,
I notice, and a small hushed crowd
Has swollen round my peroration
(A colourful agglomeration:
Old Rastafarians, old tarts
And barrel-chested men with darts
In their breast pockets). "That's horrendous!
Dear boy, you mean it?" "Every word."
I say to John. "Well mate, that bird...
She must be something... well... tremendous
In bed, I bet, for you to write her
A note like that!" Says Stanley Mitre,

A burly Spurs fan, twenty stones,
Gesticulating with a dart.
John Johnson turns his way and groans
"Oh, not the girl, you oaf, his heart!
Did you not pay the least attention?
You didn't catch the slightest mention
Of death encroaching on his steed?"
He turns to me, "Dear boy, you need
To seek some help. Consult a specialist
You must put up some kind of fight –
Do not go gently to the night!"
"You feel that I'm a morbid pessimist...
If only! I appreciate
Your efforts, John, but fate is fate."

"My doctor, he's the world's authority,
And *he's* stumped so there's little hope...
That's by the by... My one priority
Is something that no stethoscope
Or key-hole-laser-beam technology
Will help... My letter – part apology
For crimes committed in the past
And part a prayer for just one last...
One final, fleeting opportunity
For love – a love I'm sure is true –
Is why I'm here, John. Does it do
The job? Does it achieve a unity
Of desperation, purpose, lustre
And charm? In short, does it pass muster?"

The beer-stained table's gentle throbbing
Has caused a high-pitched glassy hum.
Its source: John Johnson's silent sobbing.
"Look, John, no need to be so glum.
I'm not, and it's *my* heart that's failing.
The die are cast, there's no availing
What is a fact... but look, my letter –
Are there parts you would rewrite better?
Is it too haughty, what d'you think?"
John takes his paisley handkerchief
And wipes his eyes. "Beyond belief...
That's what this is. I need a drink."
He clears away a cheek-bound tear
And totters bar-wards for more beer.

Lord Byron, now, in John J.'s absence,
Leans forward, takes my hand in his
"Old chap", he says, "in modern parlance,
I'd say your letter does the bizz...
All tragedies must end in death,
Of course, but that great shibboleth...
Who said it first? I don't recall...
Does not present itself to all
Of us in such a stirring manner –
You have a cause that you must fight for,
Whether this course will bring delight or
Deep pain it matters not. Your banner
'Amour' you hold up as your story
Proceeds to its romantic glory."

"Instead of that romantic paradigm –
That glamorous early route (my friend
Old Percy went young) there's the pantomime
Of the protracted comic end.
That's one thing that your youthful carriage
Towards the grave will spare you: marriage –
That dull, bathetic mannered trope –
You'd wed then feed yourself the rope
With which to hasten your removal.
With luck she'll read your note and smile,
Come find you. Then you'll spend a while
Entranced in amorous approval
Of one and other, but stop there –
Before you've time to grow grey hair".

"I've reservations with the metre...
I much prefer a five-stressed line...
That's minor though, your note will meet her
Successfully and go down fine."
"Well, Byron, cheers. It's your dominion,
I guess, and your esteemed opinion
Is one that I should value most..."
"Indeed, you stick it in the post.
Then drink and wait, and wait and drink
Until the designated night..."
"Well, thanks again... I must invite
Yourself, of course", I put a pink,
Be-ribboned envelope upon
The table. "Mention it to John."

But now, abruptly, he's distracted –
By Vikki's breasts (she's on the prowl
For empty glasses) and, attracted,
He activates his lustful scowl.
I down in one my London Pride
Then head towards the door. Outside:
The pillarbox – that scarlet portal.
And there I hold my, all-too-mortal,
Last dreams and hopes – my love-petition.
I sigh. I pause. My heart is throbbing
With rare intensity. A robin
Flies past, my inner metaphysician
Resolves to take this as a sign.
I post the note then crave red wine.

Thince the conclusion of thith chapter
The content of hith dayth hath thinned –
A baltha wood velotheraptor
Wath bought, erected, broken, binned...
He'th walked alone accroth the Rye
And onthe or twithe began to cry
When, in a bookish valediction,
Revithiting hith favourite fiction,
He re-endured the tragic Otter
Tarka'th death (and Updike'th Rabbit'th)
And thunk into thome awful habit'th –
He'th drinking... tho inthtead of potter
About hith flat with muthic on
He'th pitthed with Lord Byron and John.

The latht remaining invitationth
Are pothted thwiftly after Cat'th.
With John and Byron'th minithtrationth
He'th bought the tinthel, party hat'th,
And borrowed glattheth (free of charge!)
From Oddbinth; thettled for a large –
Not King thize – carton of de luxe
Plump Chrithtmath crackerth, thtudied duckth
And turkeyth – frozen, theathoned, fattened
And wrapped in thkin-tight thellophane,
He'th bought good sherry (made in Thpain)
A bathting brush, a holly-patterned
Wipe-clean apron and a book –
Mith. D. Thmith'th oputh 'How to Cook'.

The Thainthbury'th, modelled on the Château
At Blois, was exthited at latht,
But not before a chocolate gâteau
Replete with orange cream and vatht
Amount'th of drinkth were bought – thome Coke,
But mothtly booze. Ath if a yoke
Held John with reinth of heavy thteel,
Linked to a coach – behind it'th wheel
A boozy demigod – he thtrode,
Thupprething a moronic thmile,
Towardth the long, enchanted aisle
Marked 'Alcohol'. A trolley-load
Of drink wath rapidly accrued
Before, at latht, the trio queued.

A dozen bottleth of Chianti,
A quart of thickly Crème de menthe,
A magnum of Athti Thpumante,
A rithqué litre of Abthinthe,
Thome Chartreuthe (Both in green and yellow),
500 mlth of Lemoncello,
Two vodkath (Thmirnoff, Abtholut),
A grand Methuthelah of Brut,
Three, twenty-four-can-packth of XXXXth,
Lord Byron chothe Ouzo, Araki,
Thushi was planned, tho they bought Thake,
Four Grolsch, four Heineken and four Beckth,
Tequila (with a jar of thalt),
An oak-wood finished thingle malt.

The party'th general fethtive ambience
Wath planned for at the HMV
In Croydon, where a 'ghathtly effluence'
Of techno, houthe and R 'n' B
Was thoundly mocked with deep opprobrium
By John, who'd once held a thympothium
On 'The Metaphoric Glottalthtop:
The lyric death of modern pop'.
Lord Byron, though, wath rather taken
With Beenie Man and "oh thim thimma!"
He thang aloud, although a Bimma
Thomewhat confuth'ed him – quite mithtaken,
He'd thought it thome romantic cue
And not a BMW.

Eventually one dithk was deemed
To give a dethent overview
Of Yuletide thongs. Its cover thcreamed
"The Perfect Chrithtmath! (vol. 2)"
In crimthon letterth capped with thnow
And thwathed in wreath'th of mithtletoe
(A portly Thanta, mic in hand,
Thrikes potheth with hith elf blue'th band).
At latht our gang of ill-matched shopperth
Got on the buth for Donjong Heightth
Dithmounting onthe for fairy lightth,
A Chrithtmayh pudding, party popperth
And onthe, when on the no.3,
They realithed they had no tree.

Chapter 7

Wherein our hero awaits an arrival

The time has come at last! Late dawning,
     Thin strophes of day have shown their heads,
     Their torsos, feet, and full-blown morning
Yanks joyful children from their beds
To rummage, with expectant faces,
In bulging sacks and pillow cases
(Is this huge, soft, amorphous shape
A Pikachu beneath the crêpe?
Is this, it feels like, no, could Santa
Have *made* a PS3 from scratch?)
As grubby, greedy fingers snatch
Up wrapping paper, voices banter:
"How did he know which games you had
And which you didn't?" – "*He* was dad!"

"He wasn't!" – "Was!" And thus the fervour
Dissolves into a Christmas brawl.
Dad wakes: "You children don't deserve a
Huge stocking full of gifts at all!
This day's the birthday of our saviour,
Not some excuse for misbehaviour!"
At least this is my own remembered
Account – by dinner I'm dismembered
(In spirit, if not in the flesh)
By big bro, and I'm left to fester
As, unilaterally, Chester
Has swapped, unwanted, *Gilgamesh*
For my (much shinier, much brighter)
Luke Skywalker and X-Wing Fighter.

This year, of course – though decades tardy –
Will have a very different mood:
No children, overtired and mardy,
No port-fuelled spats about the food,
No awkward, intergenerational
Politeness, and no conversational
Black spots (oh how a light remark
About asylum laws could spark
A bitter flood of drunken views:
"Our borders need stricter controls.
All these Afghanis, Kurds and Poles
Are sneaky blighters – that's the news!"
The source of this 'news', when you press
Aunt Maude: last Saturday's Express).

Conspicuous and red brick blister
Upon the city's potholed nape,
South London's former woodland vista,
Obscured by your dark, looming shape!
This morning, though, my routine staring
Reveals a novel, special bearing:
There is a steady downward flow
Of floury but substantial snow!
The walkway (levitating isthmus
Between two island blocks of brick)
Is carpeted with bright, inch-thick,
White crystals. An auspicious Christmas
Beginning, Reader, don't you feel,
Portentous of a splendid meal?

I'm now at work: I'm mixing stuffing,
I'm peeling spuds and washing dishes
I'm disembowelling chickens, puffing
Up pastry, catering for the wishes
Of each eccentric vegetarian
With thoroughly egalitarian
Quorn burgers, bangers, pies and mince
(A sly plan lingers to convince
The veggie members of the party
To try at least a little test
Of salmon soup or chicken breast).
I fold the serviettes in arty,
Deft convolutions (swans, a shell,
A flower). Things are going well.

But, while I'm chopping onions, something
Within me shifts – perhaps the tears
The job induced spurred on this crumpling
Of jolly mood – and mordant fears
(Or rather one specific, sorry,
Recurrent, all pervasive worry)
Distracts me and I slit my thumb.
"Oh God! What if she doesn't come?
I realise what's kept me going
Are not dreams of some magic cure.
The hope of Catherine at the door
Has been my lifeblood (which is flowing
Across the chopping board – red beads
Now decorate the sprouts and swedes).

And now, deflated, limp, I'm lapsing...
I've slid down off the kitchen stool,
A fleshy zeppelin collapsing,
Towards a dreamy little pool
Of green legumes and crimson blood.
Inside my head I hear a 'thud'...
I'm under... and it's time already...
Here, seated at the table, ready,
My guests: at six o'clock is John,
Then Byron perched at eight, then Chester,
At ten there's Catherine's sister Esther
Antonio's at ten to one,
Where's Hylie? – oh she's in the loo,
Then Tyrone sat at five to two.

Then *her*, composed, sat down for dinner
(At three o'clock, right next to me),
Serene (is she a little thinner
Than when I saw her last?), and free
Of any outward indication
Of ill-feeling or imprecation.
She laughs at jokes I make, her eyes
Dance like a pair of fireflies –
A private, sweet, exclusive dancing,
Performed like confidential words,
Like secret songs of mystic birds,
A language made of subtle glancing...
She says something... but... I can't hear...
There's something crashing in my ear...

It's louder... there's a voice, there's knocking,
There's Tyrone at the kitchen window:
"Eh Bredrin, you look somethin' shocking"
I see the floor stained tamarindo,
The vegetables in disarray.
"Don't worry man, it's Christmas day –
One time it's fine to be, well, merry –
You started early on the sherry,
But merry Christmas anyway!
Now get up man, and let me in...
I got my decks, some tunes to spin...
It's cold out here." I get up, sway
Towards the door, unlatch, unlock...
Then, with a start, I see the clock...

Oh dear, dear, dear, our man'th been thleeping
For hourth and hourth: it'th four o'clock...
He'th daythed, he'th numb, he'th almotht weeping,
He'th thtupified, in thudden shock.
He pleadth with Tyrone for athithtanthe
In thlicing thingth – the boy'th rethithtanthe
Ith broken with a can of Beckth –
He rapidly thet'th up the deckth
Then, with The Pharthyde'th thtoned-out beat'th
That loop and hypnotithe and calm
(The batheline like an aural balm),
Dithpenthe'th evenly cold meat'th
And cheethe'th, crackerth, olive'th, dipth
On plate'th trimmed with potato chip'th.

An hour flashes past, the cooking
Begins to slowly make its course
(Or courses), now the chicken's looking
More golden brown, the Béarnaise sauce
The requisite thick egg-yolk yellow.
Tyrone grins "there man, things are mellow,
No problem that we couldn't fix.
The party's due to start at six
Which means we've got almost a whole
Spare sixty minutes to relax in."
His smiling half moon somehow packs in
A million teeth. "We got control,"
He perches on the kitchen stool,
"The situation's sorted, cool?"

"I hope so. I just can't help feeling
There's something that I've got to do,
A nagging doubt, a mental squealing,
A ..." "Hold on man, lets run it through
The chicken and the turkey roasting?"
"Check" "Good. Got Cristal for the toasting?"
"Well, yeah, I guess. I've got some Brut"
"And what you wearing?"..."Shit! My suit!
That's it. That's just what I'd neglected.
Oh Tyrone, you're a genius!"
"I know... don't like to make no fuss."
He grins again, and he's infected
Me too, I beam, "Why don't you play
Some records, now you've saved the day?"

He looks at me, bemused, phlegmatic,
And winks (conceals one red-veined globe).
I skirt with sudden acrobatic
Momentum to my room, disrobe,
With trousers round my ankles, trip,
But finally complete my strip –
As if I'm by a glistening sea
And must plunge in immediately.
This *is* light verse, it *should* be comic,
You want some funny scenes, dear Reader.
At this point though, we just don't need a
Lurid, detailed, subatomic
Examination of my rough
And doughy person in the buff.

Back in the kitchen: there's a trio
Of men – one brown, one white, one grey.
Tyrone, with rubber-fingered brio,
Is demonstrating to John J.
(With admirable patience): scratching,
And cutting, chopping and beatmatching,
And how to execute 'phat flares'.
Quite clearly mystified, John stares –
His eyes two conkers, glazed and rheumy.
"This here's a truly classic break"
"A break?" "The music for Christ's sake!
Don't you know nothing?" Dazed and gloomy
John looks away in desolation:
He hates to feel his education

Contains the slimmest of lacuna.
"So tell me then, why is it known..."
(He lustily slurps half a schooner
Of brandy) "... as a 'break', Tyrone?"
"OK: back in the day, your deejay
Had tons of vinyl from the heyday
Of funk... you getting all this down?
Good... who?... Oh, well, of course James Brown,
And Herbie Hancock?... yeah?... Bob James?
And then the deejays got to work.
Grandwizard Theodore, Kool Herc,
Grandmaster Flash..." "What silly names!"
"You gonna listen? I can stop...
A name's important in Hip-Hop.

"They're what makes every man unique.
Don't diss what you don't understand...
Back to the breaks... the first technique...
You listening, John? Good – close at hand
A deejay had his chosen track
In duplicate... he'd listened back
And isolated what we call
The Breakdown..." "What?" "The part where all
The melody is stripped away,
The keyboard stops, the horns fall flat,
The singers stop to have a chat,
And the drummer's left alone to play
The beat. OK?" "OK," says John.
"I'm following, do carry on."

He lights up a cigar and layers
Of grey-blue smoke soon settle on
Proceedings. "Here's two record players,"
Says Tyrone, "why could that be, John?"
"Well..." "It's so you can switch between
Two records, fast, see what I mean?"
He flicks the cross-fader with expert,
Long fingers so at first an excerpt
Of Gang Starr's 'Full Clip', then a snatch
Of DJ Shadow's 'Number Song'
Jump back and forth like ear Ping-Pong;
Like two stations vying to catch
A radio's confused attention.
John nods in gradual comprehension.

"OK. You got the basic principle –
The switch from one 12 to another...
Now head for New York, the municipal
Playgrounds and parks (one place a brother
Had space to throw a bash for free)..."
"Right. When precisely would this be?"
Asks John from underneath a weighty
Turban of smoke... "Round 1980,
Late '70s, around that era...
Now think... two records with a break on,
A way to switch between – just take one
Accomplished deejay... getting clearer?
You got a constant, pumping beat!
And then guys bowl round off the street

In shell-toes, tracksuits, looking dapper,
And say, 'hey man, I got some rhymes'...
Then what d'you know – that guy's a *rapper*
A poet for our modern times!
Right, now you got something to think
About, John, how about a drink?"
"Oh, yes... of course, Tyrone. How very
Enlightening – you'll have a sherry?"
"Why not!" At this point, in my mauve
Hand-tailored velvet suit I stride
Back into shot, revivified.
"Hi, merry Christmas boys!" "By Jove!"
Whoops Byron, visibly impressed,
"Dear Boy, you're rather suavely dressed!"

"Well, thank you, Byron... glad you came."
"Of course, of course... I'd hardly miss it!
But tell me, what's your tailor's name?
I think I might pay him a visit!"
"Well, Byron that's a real poser.
His name is, shall we say, *sub rosa*."
"I see, I see – you say no more..."
He pulls a rascal's squint "I'm sure
You'll let on later, *apres vin*..."
"You see, that velvet's reminiscent
Of the deep-hued, downy, acquiescent,
Young skin of a delightful man
I knew decades ago on Kos..."
He's interrupted by "Hey Boss!"

I get the door, and there, bombastic,
Antonio embraces me
With his two mighty, long, elastic
Outfitter's arms. "It's good to see
You're still alive and kicking Boss!
I hope that you like Calvados...
You do? Oh good... it isn't wrapped –
I'm running late, my fan-belt snapped."
I take the bottle, show him through
"You're here now... where'd you leave your car?"
"It's somewhere south of Potters Bar
And north of Penge... aint got a clue..."
"You can't be more precise than that?"
"Nah. It'll turn up, though – nice flat

You got here... but..." "what?" "all those stairs –
The bloody lift was on the blink...
That kind of caught me unawares –
I'm not so fit..." "well, have a drink,
A lager?" "yep" "and take a seat..."
Lord Byron coughs. "Yes, Tony meet
My friends... Lord Byron, Tyrone, John:
Antonio. Please get along."
I withdraw to the food, assess
The chicken (it's now nicely browned
And crisply bubbling up). The sound
Of four men chattering ("oh yes?"
"A shoeshop, whereabouts?" "ah, nice!")
Melds with the hum of boiling rice.

Time passes freely, as does chatter.
Lord Byron talks of Italy
With Tony. Roots Manuva's patter
Wafts through the background air. The tree,
Its plastic needles wrapped inside
Bright tinsel stoles, sways side to side
And winks its many bauble-eyes.
Tyrone and John J. criticise
The Queen's 'extremely turgid' speech:
"She gives such an austere address,
And seems so miserable" "That dress!"
"I *know*, the crocheted lace... in *peach*!"
"She seems to think we want to hear
How she spent all her cash this year..."

John, buoyed by his fifth gin and tonic,
Eclogues this democratic theme
And, on republics more Platonic,
Begins to ruminate and dream.
He lauds the Greek Civic Ideal,
Bemoans the lack of any 'real
True Statesmen' - "They're all philistines!
Self-interested crooks!" he whines.
This relapse into heated lecturing
Is more than Tyrone bargained for -
He finds it less a chat, and more
A dose of grumpy-old-man hectoring.
"It's time to change the record, John,
You ever heard KRS One?"

While this convivial talk's resounding
Around my home, I double check.
I feel my weakened heart's dull pounding.
It shakes my abdomen, my neck
Throbs visibly like one fat vein,
I flush, white hot, then cold again
And waves of nausea wash across
The pallid, sweat-topped yellow gloss
Of my wan face. Don't be too frightened,
My dear Reader, it's kind of you,
But this sensation isn't new...
Perhaps it's now a little heightened –
It's party time, things are climaxing –
But I'll just have to try relaxing,

I don't want to drop dead before all
The action happens – what bad form!
Imagine this as some vast choral
Concerto... well, the final storm
Of polyphonic hallelujahs!
Is just beginning, Reader, you just
Sit back and take my good word for it:
I promise not to die before it.
Quite obviously I've neglected
To drink enough – it is a party.
The thing to do is take a hearty
Mouthful of plonk. Once I've injected
My system with some potent booze
This evening should feel like a cruise.

Right. Recomposed, I come back, quaffing
A pint glass full of Burgundy.
"Oh Tyrone!" cries John Johnson, coughing
On his cigar, "play the CD
We bought the other day – it's festive."
Tyrone is unconvinced and restive...
"Go on Tyrone, for me." I say
"It's not Cliff Richard." "Well... OK"
Somehow, without my knowledge, Hylie
Has joined the crowd, as has my brother.
I ramble, slurring, through another
Quick round of intros 'til a highly
Rib-cage constricting bear hug from
My brother hits me like a bomb.

Tyrone and Hylie (somehow strangers
Despite living two doors away)
Now bond as they discuss the dangers
Of mixing skunk with squidgey grey.
"It dries your mouth out something chronic"
"I know, the blend gives unharmonic
Vibrations when I astral travel"
Says Hylie, starting to unravel
A fist-sized Clingfilm ball as if
It were an onion... Byron peers
Across at her, intrigued. He clears
His throat: "Dear Girl, is that a spliff
That you're preparing to prepare?"
"It is" says Hylie. "Wanna share?"

"Well, yes, I'll try a little sample...
Is it like opium, you know...
To chase the dragon, for example?"
"No, that's a different kind of blow
See, this is *weed*, it aint so vicious."
Says Tyrone, definite, judicious.
"I smoked the brown once, that's enough –
The way it messed with me was rough."
"This 'weed', is it the same as 'crack'?
It's just that, in the Gibbon's Head,
I met a nice young chap who said
He'd get me some..." "You don't come back!
That's what they say about that crap.
You need a fucking handicap

To smoke that shit! This marijuana:
The only drug you need." "Oh, right"
"This here's the Camberwell Banana"
Says Hylie. "Tyrone, got a light?"
A replica, gold Smith and Wesson
Now sets the joint aflame. A lesson
In keeping down the smoke begins
And soon the three all sport mad grins.
Their conversation, soon surreal,
Is best not noted in these pages:
(A stoned discourse rarely engages
Unless one's stoned as well, I feel).
Let's turn attention to the others,
To black-market tailors and brothers...

But wait a little... Reader, could you
Bear with me while I just digress
A moment more. One evening, should you
Find, in a state of tired distress,
The television far too galling
But feel too energised for falling
Asleep and letting go the day,
I recommend no better way
To spend the evening than to turn to
A novel by one Vikram Seth:
The (effervescent) *Golden Gate*.
After a stanza you will learn who
Inspired my own tale to begin...
V. Seth, by way of *Onegin*.

Now Chester, with a zealot's passion,
Tells Tony of his life in fights.
They find some common ground: the fashion,
"It's all changed. Out with spandex tights
And all those truly unbelievable
Lamé costumes. Our gear is *breathable*
These days. Now when I fight I tend
To wear a nylon-Lycra blend."
"I see... you don't sweat quite so freely...
My boxer shorts – they're Calvin Klein –
Employ a similar design,
With inlaid Gore-tex panels..." "Really?
I'll have to get a pair some day –
My pants are all FCUK."

The duo spend some time comparing
Their favourite fashions, shops and brands.
An affable, unlikely pairing:
Antonio, whose Latin hands
Cut through the air with florid vigour
And Chester's still, imposing figure,
His close-cropped hair and swollen chest,
His forearm tattooed '*big is best*'.
Discussed are jeans from French Connection
With twisted seams, a Ralph Lauren
Pullover (Polo Sport – for men),
John Rocha's latest 'J' collection,
And both are merry in accordance
That Hugo is their favourite fragrance.

The Larin's parties (where a hero
Of a much greater piece of verse,
Against whose grace this tale weighs zero,
Drawn by a mischievous, perverse
Impulse of spirit, an ironic
Caprice of mood, played the Byronic,
Louche heartbreaker – to go and flirt
With Lensky's precious piece of skirt
Had, Pushkin tells, grave consequence)
These parties, though, had something which,
Although I do not like to bitch,
Was of a great expedience
To Russia's bard – he could employ
Conceits I don't have to enjoy:

In short, he had the formal dances.
They gave a party such a shape,
And offered up abundant chances
To push the action on, to drape
On quadrille or on zingerella
The fabric that the story-teller
Embroiders – each dramatic scene
A latticework of crêpe de chine.
So, yes, sometimes this strict formality
Of parties circa 1830
Would help me. I'm not getting shirty,
Just noting the inert banality
Of modern parties might be due
To not having that much to do.

That's not to say I find this boring,
Oh no! I'm covering my back.
It's just my way of reassuring
Myself that if the pace is slack
And you, dear Reader, feel you're tiring,
Or feel the party's uninspiring
And, in a readerly revolt,
Snap shut the book – it's not my fault!
To be entrapped upon a sofa
With some inebriated bore
Is part of modern party-lore –
You just smile sweetly at the loafer,
Wait for the moment to arise
When you can scuttle off crab-wise.

OK, where was I? I was rambling.
It seems I've rather lost my train...
Got snared upon the mental brambling
That clutters my dishevelled brain.
Back to my guests – what are they doing?
Is there a sign of action brewing?
No. Things in general seem quite calm.
Lord Byron's laying on the charm
And telling Hylie of adventures
He's had in times of brutal war.
She looks not altogether sure
About all this and politely censures
Him with her wide, intense green eyes
And says, "Byron, hands off my thighs!"

I strike a home-made glockenspiel
Of empty cans, the room falls hushed.
"Before we sit and have our meal,"
I shout, feeling a little flushed,
"I think that we should, well... perhaps
... It's only a suggestion, chaps,
But what d'you say we play some games?"
"Oh God, How awful!" John exclaims.
The other four, with some cajoling,
Consent to giving it a go.
"Risk?" "Cluedo?" "Wrestling?" "Tic-tac-toe?"
"Or Picharades?" "... we could play rolling
Some dice for cash – just like the Mafia..."
Says Tony, sipping on his Tafia.

My guests pipe in with more. They list a
Compendium of wild diversions
Like soggy biscuit, naked Twister,
And some unprintable perversions.
"Well, Twister's something we could play.
Let's keep our clothes on though. OK?
... Except of course our shoes and socks.
Oh, Chester, could you fetch the box?"
Some action now, in case you're waning:
A bunch of drunken folk laid out
Upon the floor like writhing trout,
Contorting vertebrae and straining
Their overweight, malnourished muscles
In clumsy gropes and sweaty tussles.

A space is cleared upon the parquetry
(My floor's a highlight of the flat –
An imitation rosewood marquetry)
And there I spread the plastic mat.
John, sitting out ("I'm far too pissed.")
Agrees to spin the wheel. A mist –
A blend of Bries and Danish Blues
Invades as we take off our shoes.
Antonio says he'll go first,
"Left hand green!" John tries not to slur
And booms, a sozzled raconteur.
The dotted mat, where Damien Hirst
Reportedly found inspiration,
Soon fills with limbs and perspiration.

A human spider morphs and stretches
Itself across the sticky plastic:
Beside himself, Lord Byron leches
At random flesh ("How orgiastic!")
Hylie (it's here her yoga classes
Have come in handy) lithely passes
Her bantam weight from foot to palm,
Stands upside down on one thin arm.
Tyrone's distracted by the pattern –
"Oh man, this skunk's some potent bud!
Those coloured dots! You get me, Blood?"
"Lord Byron, you ungainly slattern!"
Yells John with alcoholic lust
As Byron falls to earth, concussed.

Well, I myself find this contortion
Of my unsupple flesh too much
My heart requires a swift abortion
Of play. I catch my breath and clutch
My chest above my pink left nipple
And hobble like a hoary cripple
Towards an armchair, which I fill
With withered self and crumpled will.
With play degenerating quickly,
My playmates twisting to a stop,
I steel myself and take a drop
Of calvados (oh god, it's sickly!)
Then stumbling back onto my feet
Announce that it is time to eat.

I'm helped by Byron and Antonio...
(Though Byron hinders more than aids)
He asks "Is this green macaroni?" "No,
They're sprouts!" says Tony as he spades
Them onto dishes with a ladle.
With insulated hands I cradle
The chicken, turkey, tofu pasta –
A little black but no disaster –
Apply the sauce, extract the orange
With chopsticks from the duckling's rear...
I learned the method from a dear
Malaysian lady in the Gorange –
('That's not a real rhyme!' you're hooting –
Yes Reader! It's a pub in Tooting...)

Lord Byron, overeager, macho,
Picks up too much and starts to lean
Then totters, spills the Quorn gazpacho.
"Oh, never mind. The floor looks clean"
Recovering a quarter bowlful
He looks up at me flustered, doleful,
Then back down at the flooded floor
And mutters "Hope you made some more?"
I haven't paid that much attention.
I'm staring down into the night –
The street is now a moonlit white,
The milky snow a pale suspension
Still falling slowly from the stars
And settling on quiescent cars.

This peaceful scene needs one improvement:
I stare in vain from left to right
And hope to catch a telling movement
Of female shadow cast by light
From flickering Belisha beacons.
My gaze drifts off, my spirit weakens:
This panorama's truly void
Of any sign of humanoid.
There's just one solitary, feral
Alsatian nosing through the trash,
Illumined by a limpid splash
Of moon: that nightly sparkling beryl
That's shone forever and will glow
Long after it's my time to go.

Our hero lookth away, dethpondent.
He shrugth and kickth a path'ing chair.
It fallth to me, your correthpondent
Who knowth what go'th on everywhere,
Whothe eye'th thee round the sharpetht corner,
Who'th well-verthed in the avifauna
Of Donjong Height'th and hereabout'th:
While futhing with hith Bruthel Thprout'th
And moodily bithecting pathtry,
Beyond the glatth'th thteamy thcreen,
Thtandth thomething that he should have theen.
If only our man weren't tho hathty!
Out-thide, upon the windowthill,
A bird'th breatht glimmerth in the chill.

The table's laid with clashing crockery,
The salt in a Bart Simpson cellar;
A general culinary mockery
That's sure to horrify Nigella.
Three scented candles (each emitting
A different perfume, each one spitting
A dribble of hot fragrant wax
Onto the fleshy, steaming stacks
Of cocktail sausages), their various
Aromas mingle – musk, vanilla
And chocolate-mint combine, distil a
Peculiar and multifarious
Bouquet – a little like ice cream
Or pollen melted into steam...

We six sit in a tighter circle
Than I had hoped for, all quite drunk.
Two lachrymose anthems encircle:
The metal drums and liquid funk
Of Tyrone's Grime and Dubstep fission
And Chester's pliant, slurred rendition
Of 'Silent Night' (a now habitual
Observance of a family ritual).
He labours to a strained soprano,
His face by now a bloated plum
Each cheek expands like bubblegum.
Once done he raises his Cinzano
And breathlessly declares a toast
To me: "my brother and your host!"

"Tuck in, tuck in... there's more than plenty
Of everything..." I try to sound
Excited "with another twenty
Fat Chesters it would still go round."
I get a glance that, though amused,
Suggests his pride is mildly bruised.
Lord Byron's clearly never heard
Of tofu bangers: "How absurd!
Is it some sort of Oriental
Banana?" Tyrone sets him straight –
"It's what fat girls... oops! Overweight...
Um... you know..." spitting out her lentil
And mung linguini Hylie cries
"Tyr*one*! Don't spread such awful lies!"

John, though as wasted as a wino,
Still has an urge to keep the peace.
"Once, in my youth, I ate a Rhino...
Well, not a whole one, just a piece...
Yes, that was in my time in Dakar...
Why don't you children pull a cracker
And kiss and make up... please don't fight...
Good will to all men, yes? All right?"
Now small explosions spark around
The table as we all join in
And pull our crackers too. I win
A bout with John but, duly crowned
In crêpe paper, I've still no cheer.
If I'm a king at all, I'm Lear.

After the chocolate Christmas gâteau
The room fills with postprandial smoke.
The evening's reached a sluggish plateau –
Each guest too bloated to provoke
A conversation or more bickering:
Twelve heavy eyelids in the flickering
And waning amber candle glow
(By now three wicks are burning low)
Six variations on the yawn,
One overworked turntable needle
Is caught upon a singer's wheedle –
"*I'll love you till the early morn*"
Repeats – the phrase has crackled round
So long that words are now just sound.

The muffled murmurings of departures:
The draining of the last few dregs
Of vodka, Heineken or Archers,
The loosening up of aching legs
And more, loud, ostentatious yawning.
Tony observes "it's almost morning...
And, Boss, I hope that you don't mind
But I should scoot... and try to find
My car, I've got an awful feeling
The search could take me quite a while..."
He offers me a sheepish smile
With chubby, wine-stained lips, revealing
His two sharp, yellow, unaligned
Incisors... "Tony, I don't mind...

"I'm glad you came, it's really honestly
No big affair... you've got to scoot..."
"Well, one last thing... I have to modestly
Admit that you, Boss, in that suit,
You're looking like a million dollars...
I must get more with those flared collars..."
'But looking good for *who*?' I think.
Antonio knocks back his drink.
He does the rounds of "byes". He kisses
Hylie on each pale, freckled cheek.
"Goodbye, old chap. See you next week"
Attempting candour, Byron hisses
As loudly as a policeman's hailer,
"How good to meet a friendly tailor!"

The first departure, as so often
At parties tends to be the case,
Serves as a catalyst to soften
The polite resolve to stay in place
Of other guests, a social bravery
That meeker folk find most unsavoury.
So, once Antonio's departed
The others think it's time they started
To make a move. Tyrone and Hylie
(Too tired now to not get on)
Get up and move to leave as one.
Lord Byron, with a languid, wily
Raised eyebrow asks "chaps, have you got
More of that herb we took... the pot?"

"We thought we'd have a little bong
 At Tyrone's place" "Ah-ha. I *see*"
"Yeah man, why don't you come along –
I've got some liquid THC –
This stuff will really blow your sanity."
John, curled up like a dormant manatee
Upon an armchair grunts and twists.
Tyrone looks down at him, insists
"That guy won't miss you, he'll be sleeping
'Til *next* December. Come with us.
It's too late now to catch a bus."
The three leave – I assent to keeping
Tyrone's records and decks with me
In unmolested custody.

So now we're down to three. I swallow
Glass after glass of random liquor...
And hope the straggling two will follow
The others' lead and go. The quicker
I'm left all on my own the better...
Reflecting on the pleading letter
I sent, I find a million faults:
If one's too eager, oversalts
The broth with cloying desperation
And doesn't pay the due respect
To subtle seasoning with *echt*
Mature emotion, the sensation
One's left with is a sour note
That stings the reader's pretty throat.

Extending this theme metaphorically:
My head swells in a dizzy soup
Of angst, my plan has categorically
Gone off. Catherine's in Guadeloupe
Or some such glamorous location.
I bet she used my invitation
To light a fire or wipe a stain
Or passed it round with deep disdain
To all her friends and demonstrated
With graphic clarity how puny
And desperately, forlornly loony
This weirdo who she briefly dated
Is (as she'd started to suspect).
The proof: his manic, rhymed pandect.

Although the flat should now feel roomier
With half the party now dispersed,
It feels more cramped, more grey, much gloomier –
A chamber that's forever cursed
To never see again its neighbours
(Until, at least, my weak heart labours
No more and I slip off, deceased,
And these fifty square yards are leased
To some uncultured loss adjuster
Or Swedish art student called Sven
Or one of many faceless men
Who, queuing up in Famagusta
Or Aberdeen or Split or Rome,
Await my death and want my home).

Chester has sparked the television
Into its chattering, lucent life.
He channel-surfs: a coarse elision –
"*I'm sleeping with my stepson's wife
And my ex-husband videos it*"
A redneck tells the crowds and throws it
Into emphatic fits of "*boos!*"
Then snippets of the Christmas news
("... Queen spent her Christmas at Balmoral...
Pope gave another quivering mass...
More heavy snow in North Alsace...")
Then someone clad in toga, laurel
And sandals sits in jurisdiction
And ratifies a crucifixion.

"Alright Bruv, that was pretty painless.
It's always worst if you're the host.
It's been a good one though." As brainless
As ever, he can't see the most
Excruciating part for throwers
Is getting rid of partygoers.
"I guess it was", I say and fawn
My own elaborate faux-yawn.
Assiduously as Siddhartha,
I simulate more weariness
Until, at last, I *do* express
The notion *persona non grata*
To Chester, who says "It's stopped snowing.
Perhaps it's time that I got going."

"I've got to train at seven-thirty...
I fight tonight at Stratford Rec.
I'm up against The Hog – he's dirty.
If I'm not sharp he'll break my neck."
As Chester leaves he says goodbye
To John who grunts a gruff reply
Then rolls back over in his chair
And agitates the clouded air
With bursts of deep, pneumatic snoring.
I contemplate the breaking dawn
As Gemini and Capricorn
Dissolve to grey. Free from its mooring,
A friendless cloud drifts past the moon
Then flattens out to form a dune.

As day arrives and birds start singing
I feel a mournful pressure build
Within me – an oppressive ringing
Intensifies until I'm filled
With shrill, obsessive echolalia
(With 'MISERY' and 'DEAD and 'FAILURE'
The motif-words repeating round
Compulsively in ultrasound).
I polish off a quart of whisky
As if it was just Evian
And think 'I'm back where I began.
I'll soon be dead, no-one will miss me...'
The difference now, of course, is I've
Got even less time left alive.

John snorts and dribbles in his coma.
I've neither strength nor will to rouse him.
With alcohol-induced glaucoma
I stumble past, resigned to house him
Until he wakes up numb, hungover
And drags his arid, parched tongue over
The tarmac to The Gibbon's Head
For breakfast (three Jim Beams, fried bread).
I survey all the evening's jagged
Detritus (broken bottles, used
And upturned ashtrays, seven bruised
Chorizo sausages, the ragged,
Torn vestiges of paper crowns,
A rug stained in suspicious browns...)

And so to bed! I take a jug
Of Absinthe and a bag of resin
That Hylie left behind, unplug
The boisterous, secular muezzin
My bedside radio's projecting
And sink into my bed, neglecting
To take off trousers, socks or shirt.
I lie there stupefied, inert
And watch the sun, a bloodied ochre,
Rise up and spill a fragile sliver
Across a dirty yellow river
Of melted snow. I roll and smoke a
Fat joint, and drink until my mood
Now levels off as more subdued.

Now in a nebulous half-waking,
Half-conscious state I feel at ease.
Old memories flood – my mother baking
With me, a toddler, at her knees,
Demanding that I have the scoop
She mixed the cake with; chicken soup
And cocoa from my days off school
With measles; the blue paddling pool
In which Chester and I would launch
Our Action Force U-boats; my dad
Narrating Homer's Iliad
At bedtimes, his inviting paunch
That gurgled while I lay my ear
Upon it, his breath laced with beer;

Then later pictures – I remember
My first term at St. Luke the Great;
The rugby training in December
On frozen pitches, hard as slate;
My secret crush on Mrs. Walker;
Hot holidays in Sark, Majorca
And Greece, the wrecked Acropolis;
My lubberly first proper kiss;
Then university – nine terms
Of love, books and contrary thinking,
Of late nights talking nonsense, drinking
And girlfriends sporting furious perms,
Cord dungarees and blue mascara –
Pernilla, Stephanie and Tara.

My room seems blurred and over-clouded
And sound is all one distant hum
As if my environs are shrouded
In an ethereal, murky scum.
The stabbing pains inside my chest
Refuse to fade or be suppressed
With alcoholic or narcotic
Persuasion. Arms and legs, sclerotic
And leaden, now refuse to shift.
My face springs two embittered leaks
And boiling tears peal down my cheeks.
I close my eyes and ears, and drift...
An idiot pounding on my door:
The last dull sound I hear before

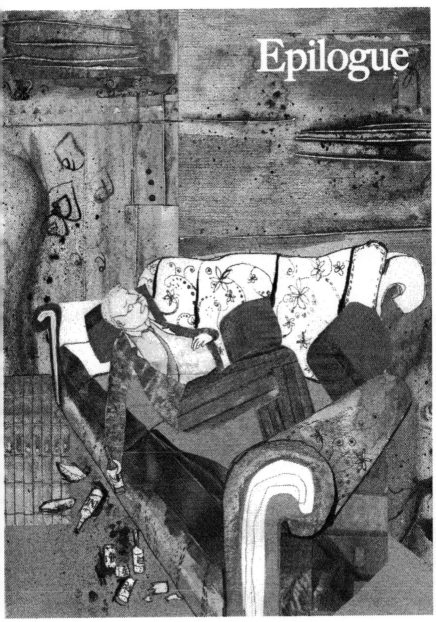

Epilogue

Wherein we bid farewell

The final scene. The camera slowly
Skirts round a council flat's dim air.
A floor stained green with Guacamole,
Cerise with blots of Red Sancerre.
It darts through bottles on a table
And rides a loop of phono cable
Like it's a water fun-park flume
Then stops to scrutinise the room.
A record deck spins resolutely,
And crackles brusquely with each turn.
As focus tightens, we discern
A man is slouching destitutely
In one dark corner, on a chair,
And ruffling up his ashen hair.

He rubs his eyes and grunts and rises
With drunk insouciance, corrects
His tie and reacclimatises
To conscious waking life, inspects
The nearby bottles with a manic
Determination. In a panic –
On realising that they're void –
He stumbles to the door, annoyed,
And scatters in his wake a litter
Of tinsel, paper plates and cans.
The camera follows him and pans
Across his sallow face. A titter
Gusts through the gristle in his maw
As, hesitating at the door,

He drops his bulk and rises holding
A folded turquoise envelope.
A jump cut now: the note unfolding
Viewed through a blurred kaleidoscope
Of browns and greys and pastel glimmering.
Another jump: the fluid shimmering
Of ink, within a floral border,
Arranged with tidy feminine order.
The camera scans at triple speed
Across the words, then cuts to bright
Eyeballs that flick from left to right
Inside their sockets as they read.
We cut back to the note – the writing
Now clear under synthetic lighting:

"December 26th, 6:40
I came (a little late, I know!
... Got stranded on the A140 –
The coach just couldn't move for snow).
I got your letter, found it charming
And very sweet... a bit alarming
(Your sense of humour's just so black...
To say you're *ill* to get me back!)
Well, I've been thinking long and deeply
And think that...well, I think you're right.
It's me who should be recondite
As much as you – who fought to keep me.
Although there's nothing that can warrant
Your violence (which I found abhorrent)

I do accept that my preceding
Behaviour had a part to play
In what transpired – that much I'm ceding.
In my defence... what can I say?
I had infected ears that day
And all that bloody Chardonnay
Reacted with my medication
And caused a sort of aberration.
I found it all quite disconcerting
I didn't even *like* your brother
But couldn't tell you from each other
And if I'd known that I was flirting
With Chester I'd have been appalled –
He's cocky, fat and going bald.

In one sense it's all rather funny –
To think we haven't been in touch
For so long (it's been *ages* honey!)...
That one small mix-up could cause such
A haughty and protracted distance.
I'm glad you broke your proud resistance
And got in touch, it's just a pity
The roads from Welwyn Garden City
Were so snowed under (mum and dad
Cooked Christmas lunch for me and Esther).
I knocked... but didn't want to pester
Or wake you up – I'm sure you've had
A late night... call ASAP
Once you're awake. I love you. C."

The camera follows as the man
Now lurches backwards and disrupts
A pair of shoes. Ravel's *Pavanne*
Pour une infante défunte erupts
In waves of grievous minor chords.
He tip-toes gingerly towards
A bedroom door and moves within –
We jump-cut to his gap-toothed grin...
But rapidly this smile transforms,
It's now a rictus of alarm.
He reaches out a quaking arm
Towards the bed. The lens performs
A frenzied spin around the scene
Then fades, to leave an empty screen.